HONO
MARRIAGE

Also available in the "How to" series:

Battle for the Mind	David Holden
Effective Evangelism	Ben Davies
Enjoying God's Grace	Terry Virgo
Facing Life's Problems	Frank Gamble
Growing Up as a Christian	Roger Day
Handling Your Money	John Houghton
Joining the Church	Richard Haydon-Knowell
Knowing God's Will	Phil Rogers
Leading a Housegroup	Richard Haydon-Knowell
Learning to Worship	Phil Rogers
Praying the Lord's Prayer	Terry Virgo
Presenting Jesus in the Open Air	Mike Sprenger
Receiving the Holy Spirit and His Gifts	Terry Virgo and Phil Rogers
Seeking the Kingdom	John Hosier

For further information on the "How to" series and other publications, please write to Frontier Publications International, 9 Boundary Road, Hove, BN3 4EH

SERIES EDITOR
TERRY VIRGO

How to...

STUDY SERIES

HONOURING

MARRIAGE

JOHN AND LIZ
WILTHEW

FRONTIER PUBLISHING INTERNATIONAL

WORD PUBLISHING
Word (UK) Ltd
Milton Keynes, England
WORD AUSTRALIA
Kilsyth, Victoria, Australia
WORD COMMUNICATIONS LTD
Vancouver, B.C., Canada
STRUIK CHRISTIAN BOOKS (PTY) LTD
Maitland, South Africa
ALBY COMMERCIAL ENTERPRISES PTE LTD
Balmoral Road, Singapore
CHRISTIAN MARKETING NEW ZEALAND LTD
Havelock North, New Zealand
JENSCO LTD
Hong Kong
SALVATION BOOK CENTRE
Malaysia

HONOURING MARRIAGE
© John and Liz Wilthew 1991.
Published by Word (UK) Ltd. / Frontier Publishing International.

ISBN 0-85009-188-8   (Australia 1-86258-167-3)

Unless otherwise indicated, Scripture quotations are from the New
International Version (NIV). Copyright © 1973, 1978, 1984 by
International Bible Society.

Reproduced, printed and bound in Great Britain for Word (UK) Ltd. by
Richard Clay Ltd., Bungay.

91 92 93 94 / 10 9 8 7 6 5 4 3 2 1

FOREWORD

The "How to" series has been published with a definite purpose in view. It provides a set of workbooks suitable either for housegroups or individuals who want to study a particular Bible theme in a practical way. The goal is not simply to look up verses and fill in blank spaces on the page, but to fill in gaps in our lives and so increase our fruitfulness and our knowledge of God.

Both of Peter's letters were written to "stimulate ... wholesome thinking" (2 Peter 3:1). He required his readers to think as well as read! We hope the training manual approach of this book will have the same effect. *Stop*, *think*, *apply* and *act* are key words.

If you are using the book on your own, we suggest you work through the chapters systematically, Bible at your side and pen in hand. If you are doing it as a group activity, it is probably best to do all the initial reading and task work before the group sessions — this gives more time for discussion on key issues which may be raised.

Unless otherwise stated, all quotations from the Bible are from the New International Version which you are, in the main, encouraged to use when you fill in the study material.

Terry Virgo
Series Editor

Special Thanks

Writing a book is more of a team effort than we imagined. Thanks to Arnold Bell for his careful scrutiny of the manuscript, to David Rigby whose recommendations have made this a much better book, and to everyone we have overworked throughout the whole process!

Frontier Publishing International is committed to the production of printed and recorded materials with the view to reaching this generation with the gospel of the kingdom. FPI is part of New Frontiers International, a team ministry led by Terry Virgo, which is involved in planting and equipping churches according to New Testament principles. New Frontiers International is also responsible for a wide range of training programmes and conferences.

Contents

Introduction

Honouring Marriage is a workbook designed to be flexible enough for a husband and wife to use in the privacy of their own home, or for local church leaders to use with one couple or a group of couples.

The material was taken from a series of Marriage Courses which we conducted in our own church in Brighton. The material has been developed for the printed page, but many couples who have been through our "Wise before the Event", "One Year On" and "Marriage Enrichment" courses have played their part in testing what you are about to read.

There are some excellent marriage courses and books available now, and we have learned a great deal from them. Our aim, however, has been to provide something biblical and practical which generates communication between husband and wife, and yet can still be a resource for use in the local church. We have tried to intrude as little as possible, preferring that couples talk about their marriage rather than read about ours or other people's marriages.

Potential readers need to know from the outset that this book will be demanding in terms of time, effort and commitment. In our experience it is men who especially need to take this seriously. When one partner approaches the material in a shallow way, it will be extremely frustrating and discouraging for the other who believes that marriage is worth more than that.

We hope that ministers and pastors will find this a helpful tool as they give support to married couples in their churches. Those who wish to help couples review and enhance their marriages before major crises threaten, will find this book particularly useful. It should be possible to make two or three short marriage courses out of the material, adapting the chapters to the needs of the couples with whom they are working.

The subject of *Honouring Marriage* has always been important but it is particularly vital today when little stigma is attached to "living together", extramarital affairs are commonplace, and divorce is there as an ejector seat for the couple who hit difficulties. Christian couples, like everyone else, need encouragement to see how important their marriages are.

The New Testament word "honour" is associated with the idea of estimating the value of something. In fact, the very same word is used of the Lord Jesus Christ Himself when He is described as "crowned with glory and honour" (Heb 2:7,9; cf 2 Pet 1:17). God Himself has made His evaluation of marriage; it is to be "honoured by all" (Heb 13:4).

Honouring Marriage therefore, must be one of the highest priorities for every husband and wife. This book aims to help you know "How to..."

John and Liz Wilthew

Chapter 1 SOLID GROUND TO BUILD ON

Almost everyone marries! Although the death of marriage as an institution has been forecast for years, it is still alive and kicking. In the UK for example, only one woman in twenty and one man in eleven remains single by the age of forty, and even the majority of young men and women who live together go on to be married. Evidently the majority regard marriage as highly desirable.

At the same time the divorce rate is alarmingly high, and countless couples endure rather than enjoy being married. A common caricature of marriage is a besieged city, with all those outside wanting to get in, and all those inside wanting to get out. This hardly reflects an honouring of marriage!

If most people want to be married and yet many end up disillusioned, it is difficult to avoid the conclusion that marriage is not all it is made out to be. Perhaps that is exactly it! Most people harbour expectations of marriage that are unrealistic. How many times have you heard someone say, "All I ever wanted to do was to get married"? Behind these apparently harmless words may lie a Disney-like fantasy, the idea that marriage itself is the doorway to being "happy ever after".

Yet, it is possible for couples to enjoy a superb marriage. Many successful marriages, perhaps even your own, are clear demonstrations of this. But such successes are rooted in the real world rather than in the pursuit of illusions.

In this opening chapter we will take a look at the only one hundred per cent solid ground on which to build your marriage as we set out to explore how to honour marriage.

Start by reading Matthew 7:24-27. Here we have a parable about obedience to Jesus and His Word. It deals with the importance of foundations. The foundation on which you intend to build your life is of vital significance. The parable is all about two houses which look the same. Both face the same fierce conditions; one stands securely while the other crashes in ruins. The big difference between the two is beneath surface level, in the foundations.

In the New Testament, the word translated "house" may be used, not only of a dwelling place but of the household living within it. The same word can refer to either bricks and mortar (house) or the family (household). With this in mind read the passage again, substituting "family" every time the word "house" appears.

Weak Foundations
The following exercise will help you to think about what it means to build a household on sand.

Imagine that you and your spouse work as a successful husband and wife team on the Agony column of a popular weekly magazine. You are Henrietta and Humphrey, the celebrated agony aunt and uncle of the nation. In today's massive postbag you have, by sheer coincidence, received two letters: one from a husband and the other from his wife. It is clear that each partner has written without the knowledge of the other.

Here are the two troubled letters.

Station Road, Newtown

Dear Henrietta and Humphrey,
After only two years my marriage is a real disappointment. When I first met Jim we were both students at the Poly, and he was such fun to be with. In fact, he was quite a catch! I remember how some of my friends were green with envy because he was so good looking and romantic, and he seemed to be successful at just about everything.

But after six months of marriage he began to change. With our friends he was the same charming Jim, but when we were alone he became quiet

12

and tense, and from that time on there has not been much laughter or enjoyment in our marriage.

If I try to get him to talk he's either too tired or too busy. When we were courting he would often tell me how much he loved me, but he hardly ever says anything like that now. I can't remember the last time he noticed my hair or my clothes or said that I looked nice.

How can he have changed so much? Do you think that he no longer loves me? I don't understand him any more.

Everybody looks on us as the perfect young married couple, but if only they knew.

I do love him, but if things go on this way I can't see our marriage surviving. Please can you help me to find the Jim I used to know.

Please change our names and don't mention our address if you publish this letter.

Yours,
   Jenny

Station Road, Newtown

Dear Humphrey and Henrietta,

I never imagined that I would ever write to a column like yours, but the truth is I have no-one I can turn to. My marriage is in difficulty. I know it is probably my fault, but I feel totally helpless to do anything about it.

My friends and even my wife Jenny have this image of me as the life and soul of the party. Everyone expects the smile, the joke, the clever quip. No-one ever thinks that I'll make a mess of anything. "Jim's a winner", that's what my college pals used to say.

Yet, the truth is very different. Inside I feel inadequate and full of fear. I could hardly believe it when Jenny fell for me at college, and all through our courting and engagement I half expected her to be whisked off by someone else. We did get married, but Jenny didn't know the real me, just my facade of confidence.

I thought I could keep up the bluff, but I can't. Now I see my marriage slipping through my fingers.

I know Jenny is disappointed with me, and sometimes, when I see her talking to another man, I think that she could well go off with someone else one day.

What do you suggest? I want my marriage to work, and yet I'm afraid that if I'm open and honest with her she may not want me as I really am.

Please preserve my anonymity.

Yours sincerely,
   Jim

Having read the two letters, first talk over together the various areas of hurt, disappointment and fear in the couple's relationship. As you do so, write anything you identify below:

....

....

....

....

....

Having done this, look beneath the surface at any weak foundations you are able to detect. In other words, what has caused the hurts, disappointments and fears you have listed above? Make a list of them. (If you want help at this point, consult Appendix 1, where you will find some suggestions to guide you.)

....

....

....

....

....

14

These foundations are just not strong enough, even though they may appear to be for a time. Check through the following list of weak foundations, and begin to ask yourself whether you are building on sand.

Romantic love and emotion:	marriage as one long honeymoon
Material prosperity:	beautiful home and possessions, good salary and comfortable lifestyle
Self-interest:	someone to love "me", provide for "me" and look after "me"
Conditional love:	"I will love you *if*..."
Escape clause:	availability of divorce if things don't work out
Charm and personality:	pleasantness and sense of humour rather than character
Sexual attraction:	physical beauty and passion

Solid Foundations

While the foolish man built his house on sand, the wise man built on rock. Look up the parallel passage in Luke's gospel (Luke 6:46-49) and notice a phrase there which sums up the difference. Write it out below.

"He is like a man building a house, who...
and laid the foundation on rock" (Luke 6:48).

The irony of the story is that the foolish builder probably thought the other was the stupid one! After all, digging down deep took much more time, effort and resources.

Both houses looked identical, so what was the point of all that extra activity? The answer became clear the moment the torrent struck!

Write out verse 47. It is an important statement because Jesus is describing the "wise man" and explaining what it means to build on a solid foundation.

"
....

....

....
"

Your life must be built on Jesus Christ Himself.
Popular wisdom says to those entering marriage, "You will have to learn to adjust to one another". That is sound common sense. However, Scriptural wisdom is radical! It maintains that a successful marriage is more about two people adjusting to a third person — Jesus Christ. When you are both in line with Him you will find that you are on solid ground. If one, or both, of you are out of line with Him then you will start to shake!

Think about the following statements and indicate with a tick which ones, in your judgement, reveal a life established on the foundation of Jesus Christ.

I know I am a child of God because:
- ❑ I pray every night.
- ❑ I was brought up in a Christian home.
- ❑ Jesus is the most important person of all to me.
- ❑ My life is no longer rooted in self-interest but in a desire to follow Christ.
- ❑ I attend church regularly.
- ❑ My attitudes and behaviour are becoming more Christ-like.
- ❑ Everything seems to go right for me these days.
- ❑ I don't have much fun any more!
- ❑ Jesus Christ died on the cross for my salvation.
- ❑ One of my chief delights now is to worship.
- ❑ I do a lot of voluntary work for charity.
- ❑ Doing things for others is no longer a chore since I realised what Jesus did for me.

Now take a look at these reactions to a crisis and tick those which apply to you. Answer honestly!

My first responses when I hit serious problems are:
❑ To question God's goodness.
❑ To doubt my faith.
❑ To make tracks for my minister, elder or group leader.
❑ To get on my knees and turn to Christ.
❑ To grit my teeth and rely on my own resources and ingenuity.
❑ To ask my partner to pray for me.
❑ To scream and shout and make sure everyone knows.
❑ To encourage myself by filling my mind with appropriate passages of Scripture.
❑ To expect my partner to have the answer.
❑ To remember that God's grace is my security; He is "for" me.

Compare your answers with your partner later.

Your life is also to be built on Truth.
God's word is to be the solid ground you stand upon. As the Holy Spirit helps you to understand God's will and ways through the Bible, your behaviour, values, attitudes, goals, decisions and lifestyle will be affected.

According to Matt 7:24-27 both the wise and foolish man hear Christ's words. Write down what distinguishes them:

"everyone who hears these words of mine...

.... is like a wise man who built his house on the rock"

How did the following Biblical couples respond to God's word to them, in ways that had repercussions for them and the whole of history?

17

Adam and Eve (Genesis 2:16,17)

....

....

....

Abram and Sarai (Genesis 12:1-3)

....

....

....

Joseph and Mary (Matthew 1:20,21)

....

....

....

When faith in Christ and obedience to His word is the foundation of your lives you will be able to build a "house" which will stand. He makes a fundamental difference to your relationship with one another in the following ways.

(i) You look at yourself differently
The way you see yourself is of crucial importance to your marriage. What is *your* estimate of yourself? Here is an exercise to give you a quick "reading". Make a list of your strengths and weaknesses. Don't "agonise" over it: write the things which spring most readily to mind.

Strengths   **Weaknesses**

....

....

....

....

18

How does your list look? Have you been able to identify your strengths alongside your weaknesses, or have you ended up with a long list of weaknesses and a "token" item in the strengths column?

A low view of yourself is one of the most dangerous pieces of baggage you can carry into married life. It combines a sense of uselessness and worthlessness with the distorted idea that to be loved by your partner you must never fail, constantly live up to expectations, and always compare favourably with others. In short, you have to be perfect! With this can come an inability to love and accept a partner who is less than perfect.

As you (and your partner) inevitably fall short of this exacting standard a variety of destructive symptoms appear (eg jealousy, super-sensitivity, inconsistency, fear, defensiveness, living in retreat, anger, unforgivingness, depression, and an inability to trust). Not a pretty picture is it? It is no wonder that this leads to marriage difficulties!

When your life is built on Jesus Christ there is no reason for you to feel you are worthless. Check the following list of ways in which God has made it possible for you to have a positive view of yourself.

* I am so valuable that Christ gave His life on the cross for me. God has shown how much He thinks I am worth! (1 Pet 1:18,19)
* As a "new creation" in Christ, God is restoring His own image in me. (Col 3:10)
* I am accepted by God on the basis of grace — unconditionally and irrevocably. (Eph 2:4-9)
* God gives the Holy Spirit to minister His love deep into my spirit. (Rom 5:5)
* I am a "partaker" of the divine nature! (2 Pet 1:3-4)

(ii) You look at your partner differently
For those whose dominating desire in life is personal happiness a

marriage partner might appear to be the answer. The trouble with this is that, however 'nicely' it is done, the relationship is motivated by self-interest. One person expects the other to satisfy their needs.

Personal needs are not sinful of course. You have emotional needs which must be met. But you can fall into the trap of looking entirely to your partner to meet those needs. We experienced this one year into our marriage, as *Liz* now explains.

"When we moved to Sheffield I found myself in a part of the country which was completely different from my home area. There were no familiar friends or family members nearby and I felt very lonely and isolated and soon became depressed.

"During this time God also seemed far away. It was very hard for John to help me out of my depression. Then one day, as I was praying, God showed me that I had been depending far too heavily on John to meet my spiritual needs. At the same time He reminded me of John's need for my active help and support in his ministry. I realised that I had to trust the Lord to meet my own needs while I concentrated on being a support to John as he adjusted to the demands of his new role as a pastor. For me this was the turning point."

Take a look at the list below. Which of these (or other) needs are most important to you, and your partner? Number the top three in both columns.

	Self	Partner
acceptance	....	....
value	....	....
security	....	....
approval	....	....
understanding	....	....
fellowship	....	....
....	....	....
....	....	....

20

Now look up the following Scriptures and write them in the appropriate spaces. Each of them underlines that Jesus Christ is the One who meets your deepest needs.

Matthew 11:28

....

....

....

John 15:9

....

....

....

Hebrews 4:16

....

....

....

With Jesus Himself as the foundation of your life you are able to look at your partner as someone to be loved and cared for, rather than someone to love and care for you. The driving force in your life is no longer to seek love but to give it.

This may seem threatening to some couples. After all, if Jesus is the One who meets your intimate needs will that not take something away from your husband/wife relationship? Should you not expect your partner to love and care for you? Are you prohibited from ever again saying those lovely words, "I need you"?

On the contrary, as you both develop your own deep relationship with Christ, you not only bring the benefits of this to your spouse, you receive benefits too! The Lord Jesus Christ makes you the person your partner needs, and makes your partner the person you need. Intimate fellowship with Christ becomes the key to deeper fellowship with one another — which every marriage needs.

Here are a few examples of right and wrong expressions of need in marriage. Can you add others?

Right	Wrong
1. I need your love.	1. Without your love I'm finished!
2. I need you to complement me.	2. I'm not a whole person without you.
3. I need you to be an avenue of God's grace.	3. I'm utterly dependent on you.
4. I need you more than anyone else.	4. You are more important to me than Jesus Christ Himself.
5. I need you to share my life.	5. My life revolves around you.
6. I need you to keep encouraging me in my faith.	6. I rely on your faith in God.

Right	Wrong
....	....
....	....
....	....
....	....

Each wrong expression of need reveals a life that is not "rooted and built up" in Christ (Col 2:6,7), while every right expression of need is compatible with a life in which Jesus is Lord. No matter how wonderful your partner may be, he/she will fail you at times. Christ never fails you.

Assignment

As a couple compare your answers to the two lists, "I know I am a child of God because...", and "My first responses when I hit serious problems are..." Talk over any areas of uncertainty. Where you have made different responses, seek to understand why. If you have both answered with total honesty (rather than simply having ticked "the right answer"), there may be areas of weakness or vulnerability over which you can pray together. Check your responses against those in Appendix 1.

Finally, as Henrietta and Humphrey, talk together about how Jim and Jenny of Station Road, Newtown should proceed. What will you be writing in your "Agony column"?

The word "wedding" is derived from the Anglo-Saxon "wed" meaning a pledge. This chapter takes you through the words of the Marriage Service, looking especially at the serious vows and pledges you made on your wedding day. Keeping these vows is fundamental if you are to honour marriage.

There may have been some variation in the words used in your service, but the following declarations and promises form the backbone of most Marriage Ceremonies. We will explore them together with a particular eye for any Biblical background.

But first, take time to consider the way that, throughout the Marriage Service, questions are addressed to the man before the woman. Why is this? The order reflects a Biblical perspective on the husband/wife relationship which can be traced back to the first man and woman.

In the Beginning
Look up Genesis 2:4-23 and read it together. Notice how:

1. God created the man first — not momentarily (as one twin might emerge before the other) but a substantial period before. Complete the following verses.

"The Lord God...

....

....

...." (v.15)

"And the Lord God..

....

....

....

....

...." (vv.16,17)

Adam had the opportunity to establish his relationship with God before entering into a relationship with anyone else. In this period he could come to terms with how special he was to God— how loved, valued and cared for. Out of this unique relationship he would be able to give himself to another.

2. God created the woman for the man. Even though his relationship with God was wonderful, Adam still needed others. Notice who asserts this!

"..

....

...." (v.18)

Adam was no doubt very grateful for rabbits, reindeers and ravens, but somehow they were not what he needed. Indeed, as he named the creatures around him, he must have worked out that he was something of an oddbod! Every other living creature had a mate.

So God made Eve. She was created with a special function in mind. What word does the Scripture use to describe this? (See vv.18 and 20).

....

....

....

There is nothing lowly or demeaning about this description of a woman's purpose and function in marriage. On the contrary:
* It underlines the man's sense of need and emphasises the woman's inherent value (she is more than a childbearer).
* The word "helper" gives the woman dignity and honour because it is frequently used of God Himself.

3. God created the woman out of the man. Eve was not made out of the earth like Adam and the other living creatures (vv. 7 and 19). Complete the verses below:

"Then the Lord God..

....

....

....

....

....

...." (vv. 22,23)

You will find that the apostle Paul identifies each of these three aspects of Adam's priority in creation (1 Timothy 2:13; 1 Corinthians 11:8,9). He understands each to show the spiritual headship of a man in relation to a woman, a husband in relation to his wife. Adam was to be a strong spiritual leader, something for which his relationship with God had prepared him. Eve was to enjoy his loving, godly authority.

Write out 1 Corinthians 11:3.

".. .

....

...."

27

In the husband/wife relationship there is a reflection of that perfect authority and subordination between God the Father and God the Son.

So, in the Marriage Service the bridegroom precedes the bride in his declarations and promises. At your wedding each of you made equally serious vows, but the man stood in the place of the initiator and the woman responded. The same pattern can be seen in God's relationship to His people.

Write out Hosea 2:19,20.

"..

....

....

....

....

...."

An Important Question
As the minister asked the following question, each of you responded with "I will":[1]

".. will you take .... to be your wife (husband)? Will you love her (him), comfort her (him), honour and protect her (him), and, forsaking all others, be faithful to her (him) as long as you both shall live?"

Look carefully at the wording. How does this question appear to you now that you are well and truly married? Talk together as a couple (or a group) and record any helpful insights. A selection of Scriptures has been given to help your discussion.

Talk about what it means to love your partner as a husband/wife. (John 15:12; 1 Cor 13:4-8; Eph 5:22,23; 1 Pet 3:1-6)

Give some examples of comfort, honour and protection in marriage. (Gen 24:67; Prov 31:28,29; Eccles 4:9-12; 1 Pet 3:7)

Why is lifelong faithfulness to your marriage partner so important? (Prov 3:3,4; Mal 2:13-15; Matt 19:1-6; Heb 13:4)

Leaving to Cleave

The bride's father almost certainly had a special place of significance at your wedding. First of all, he demonstrated his willing consent to the marriage by processing with his daughter and bringing her to the bridegroom. Do you remember how you felt at that moment? Then, in his brief declaration, the father transferred responsibility for the welfare of his daughter to you, her husband.

The father's special role is an echo of the very first "wedding". Look again at Genesis 2, this time at verses 22-24. Having created a woman from Adam, God Himself "brought her to the man". The words on marriage which follow are among the most important in the Bible (v.24). They form the basis of the teaching of both Paul and the Lord Jesus Christ Himself (Eph 5:31, Matt 19:5).

Write them below.

"..

....

....

....

....

...."

Following the King James (Authorised) version of the Scriptures, this is often referred to as "leaving", "cleaving" and "becoming one flesh". Marriage is meant to draw you closer to your partner than to any other human being.

1. "A man will leave his father and mother..."
Behind the legal ceremony lies a leaving of your parents. This is more important than many people realise. When parents of one of the marriage partners are reluctant to "let go", they can expect heartache! Talk about the different parental attitudes in Genesis 24:50-66 and 1 Samuel 18:12-29; 19:8-17 and the consequences for the newly-weds.

This subject of "leaving" will be explored in more depth in Chapter 6, "Family Connections".

2. "...and be united to his wife..."
Some years ago the newspapers reported a remarkable visit of a wife, to her husband who was "enjoying" HM Prison's hospitality. When visiting time ended, they could not be parted; she had stuck herself to her man with superglue!

To be "united" in marriage is to be stuck like glue to one another. The marriage vows themselves play an important part in this deep joining of husband and wife. What word does the Bible use to describe the strong bond that unites you? Write out the following Scripture and underline the key word.

"She is your partner, ...

...." (Mal 2:14)

Now take a look at the following ingredients of this marital glue:

acceptance	responsibility	loyalty
trust	commitment	faithfulness
steadfastness		

List any other ingredients you can think of.

....

....

....

You will see from Malachi 2:13-16 how seriously God regards divorce. It is covenant breaking ("you have broken faith with her") and a tearing apart of those whom God has joined ("has not the Lord made them one?")

3. "...and they will become one flesh"
Marriage makes it possible for you to develop your relationship with each other to an exclusive level of intimacy.

What does this word "intimacy" indicate? Talk together and try to come up with a definition. If you have a dictionary or a thesaurus, see how they define it and what examples they offer.

....

....

....

31

Becoming "one flesh" means *physical* intimacy. God gave you the gift of sex as a wedding present so that you could "know" each other. This "one flesh" intimacy will explore new depths of "knowing" when you develop *emotional* and *spiritual* intimacy alongside the physical. We will also look at each of these in more detail in later chapters. For the present, write out Genesis 2:25 below.

"

....

....

....

...."

Adam and Eve enjoyed this level of intimacy before sin damaged their relationship with God.

The Vows
The following vows are included in most wedding services, although you may have added others of your choice. They can be summed up in three words.

Firstly, they are *voluntary*. The opening declaration expresses a deliberate, thoughtful choice of your marriage partner, and a decision to live by the terms of the Marriage Covenant. **"I .... take you ....to be my wife (husband), to have and to hold from this day forward..."** Make a list below of those things you chose to leave behind when you became husband and wife.

living alone   ....

pleasing myself   ....

....

....

....

Remember, no one forced you to do this. It was your free decision!

Secondly, your commitment was an *unconditional* one. It was **"for better, for worse, for richer, for poorer, in sickness and in health..."** Your promises were not dependent on circumstances. This is one of the reasons why we refer to Christian marriage as a covenant rather than a contract. Unforeseen circumstances do not provide an escape clause. Instead, they provide fresh opportunities for love to deepen and mature.

The vows recognise that many of these "unforeseens" will be very pleasant indeed. Take time to talk together about some of the highlights of your married life so far. What are some of your happiest memories?

While married life produces a store of wonderful memories and many lovely surprises, it also faces circumstances which require flexibility, mutual support and understanding. Some of these are listed below. Which of them have you experienced? Go through the list together and tick as appropriate.

- ❏ accommodation problems
- ❏ pregnancy and first child
- ❏ miscarriage
- ❏ infertility
- ❏ job change
- ❏ church change
- ❏ more children
- ❏ postnatal depression
- ❏ house move
- ❏ move to different part of country
- ❏ serious ill-health
- ❏ unemployment
- ❏ bereavement
- ❏ menopause
- ❏ debt
- ❏ dependent relatives
- ❏ children getting married
- ❏ retirement
- ❏ move to different part of world

Now separately, write a few sentences overleaf about the effect on your marriage of anything you have identified. Then show each other what you have written, and talk about it together.

....

....

....

....

....

....

Thirdly, your vows are *permanent*. Marriage is a covenant **"to love and to cherish till death us do part, according to God's holy law, and this is my solemn vow"**. Do you remember which words of Jesus were quoted by the officiating minister as he pronounced you to be husband and wife? You will find them recorded in Matthew 19:3-8.

"Therefore..

...."

Your union is permanent because God has joined you. You cannot disown it when you hit difficulties or realise your partner isn't perfect after all, or because you like the look of someone else. This does not mean that you should regard marriage as a life sentence! Permanence is one of the most important ingredients of all for healthy personal growth and developing relationships. Below is a sample of the human needs God intends to be met through lifelong marriage.

* the growth of mutual understanding
* acceptance of a person "warts and all"
* channelling of sexual desires into something creative (intimacy) and character-building (fidelity and self-control)
* facing up to difficulties from a secure base
* stable environment for bringing up children

Each of these could be explored at greater length. Why not take some time to talk about them together (or as a group)?

The Wedding Ring

As you slipped (or squeezed) the wedding ring onto your partner's finger, you repeated these, or similar, words: **"I give you this ring as a sign of our marriage. With my body I honour you, all that I am I give to you, and all that I have I share with you, within the love of God — Father, Son and Holy Spirit".**

What does the wearing of a wedding ring mean to you? Talk about the significance it has for you.

As this chapter closes, read through the following extract from a famous sermon. Dietrich Bonhoeffer was imprisoned and then executed on the orders of Adolf Hitler just before the end of the Second World War. In *Letters and Papers from Prison* the editor has included "A Wedding Sermon from a Prison Cell", written by Bonhoeffer in 1943. The sermon deserves to be read in its entirety, but here is an extract which spells out the honour with which God has invested marriage. Underline any sentences which stand out for you, and talk them over together.

"Marriage is more than your love for each other. It has a higher dignity and power, for it is God's holy ordinance, through which he wills to perpetuate the human race till the end of time. In your love you see only your two selves in the world, but in marriage you are a link in the chain of the generations, which God causes to come and to pass away to his glory, and calls into his Kingdom. In your love you see only the heaven of your happiness, but in marriage you are placed at a post of responsibility towards the world and mankind. Your love is your own private possession, but marriage is more than something personal — it is a status, an office. Just as it is the crown, and not merely the will to rule, that makes a king, so it is marriage, and not merely your love for each other, that joins you together in the sight of God and man. As you first gave the ring to one another and have now received it a second time from the hand of the pastor, so love comes from you, but marriage from above, from God. As high as God is above man, so high are the sanctity, the rights, the promise of marriage above the sanctity, the rights, and the promise of love. It is not your love that sustains the marriage, but from now on, the marriage that sustains your love."[2]

Assignment

Chart the development of your marriage using any photos you may have. Start with the earliest pictures of the two of you prior to your wedding, and then proceed through to the present time. You may want to make a special album consisting of one photo from each different stage of your life together. As you select the photographs, identify your circumstances and feelings at those times.

Notes

[1] The *Alternative Service Book 1980* is copyright © The Central Board of Finance of the Church of England. Extracts are reproduced with permission.

[2] Dietrich Bonhoeffer, *Letters and Papers from Prison* (Edited by Eberhard Bethge). Enlarged, revised edition. SCM Press Ltd. (1971), pp. 42-43. Reproduced with permission.

Marriage contracts are becoming commonplace in many European countries as well as in America. An increasing number of couples now make a pre-nuptial visit to their solicitor to sort out who gets what in the event of divorce.

Many of these contracts also include lifestyle clauses. Have you strong opinions about who washes the dishes, the occupation of the bathroom and evenings out with "the lads"? Yes? Well then, you can include them in your contract.

The real issue behind the contract is clear enough. What if matrimony turns to acrimony involving alimony?

Looking full in the face of divorce statistics such couples are making arrangements for parting. From time to time a spectacular romantic bust-up in Hollywood brings one of these contracts under the spotlight, usually because of the multi-million dollar settlement involved.

Pre-marital contracts have little force in English law as it stands because the marriage ceremony is deemed to supersede such agreements. There is, however, a pressure group fighting for the law to be changed. If they have their way, the marriage service will eventually include those meaningful words, "subject to contract".

As we have already seen, God views marriage as a covenant rather than a contract. Many of the issues raised by pre-marital contracts are, of course, important. Couples should face up to the facts about marriage difficulties. They do need to be clear about their expectations of each other once married and it is essential that they discuss their views on children, politics, finances, faith etc. But, once those vows have been made, marriage is unconditional and permanent. The couple have entered into a solemn and binding covenant.

This covenant is all the more serious because it involves someone other than the husband and wife. Write out the following scriptures, and then underline the key phrases which identify the other party.

"...
....
....
....
...." (Prov 2:16,17)

"...
....
....
....
....
....
....
....
...." (Mal 2:14,15)

God's Covenant Love

God Himself is a witness to your covenant in marriage, both as an onlooker and a perfect example. You are never asked to be or do anything that is not already a glorious part of His nature and activity.

Throughout the Scriptures God initiates and reaffirms covenant love towards His chosen people. He makes important covenant promises:

* to Noah   (Gen 6:18)
* to Abraham   (Gen 17)
* to Moses   (Ex 24)
* to David   (2 Sam 7)

More generally, God's covenant love is described in terms of marriage to His bride, Israel. Look at Ezekiel 16:8-14 and write out verse 8.

"..

....

....

....

....

...."

But it is in Hosea's ministry that this great theme is seen most dramatically .The prophet was called to live out the message of God's covenant love in his own marriage to an unfaithful wife.

According to Hosea 1:2,3 he was instructed to marry Gomer knowing either that she was already a promiscuous woman, or that she would become one. God had entered into covenant with Israel in the same knowledge, that she would be unfaithful to Him. After bearing two sons and a daughter (only the first son is clearly said to be Hosea's), Gomer seems to have deserted the prophet, ending up as a prostitute in poverty and slavery. Read Chapter 3 to find out what happened, and then write out God's reaffirmation of His covenant love to promiscuous Israel in 2:19,20.

"...
....
....
....
....
...."

Yet God longed for a pure, faithful bride. It was with this in mind that God spoke through the great prophets of a radically different kind of covenant, one which would change the hearts of His people. You will find this promise of a new covenant in Jeremiah 31:31-34. Write out verse 33 below.

"...
....
....
....
....
...."

It was the Lord Jesus Christ who brought this new covenant into being. By His atoning death on the cross He made it possible for men and women to live transformed lives (see Hebrews 10:11-16). Write out the memorable words of Jesus spoken at His Last Supper.

"...
....
...." (Luke 22:20)

While this covenant love is wonderfully personal, it is also corporate. Christ gave His life for the church, His bride. The apostle Paul writes about this to the believers at Ephesus, concluding that it is a "profound mystery" (Eph 5:22-33). What does he say about Christ's new covenant love for His bride, the church?

"..

....

....

....

....

....

...." (Eph 5:26,27)

The words that you have just written deserve special attention. They are a breathtaking description through which Paul may be reflecting four stages of courtship:

a) **Romance**: No bride has ever been wooed with such love. "Christ loved the church and gave Himself up for her" (Eph 5:25). In fact, the young lady in question was far from lovable! She was neither beautiful, pure, nor interested in Him. Yet everything Christ gave up, everything He suffered and everything He achieved on the cross was to win her as His bride.

b) **Betrothal**: At betrothal a Jewish bride-to-be was legally set apart to belong to the groom. She was no longer regarded as a single woman, nor was she free to enjoy the attention of other would-be suitors. So too Christ's great love for the church was "to make her holy", ie to separate her to Himself. It should be obvious to whom we belong as the bride of Christ. Our devotion to Jesus and rejection of the world's values should mark us out as different.

41

c) Preparation: Between betrothal and the wedding the couple kept themselves pure by faithfulness, developed their relationship with one another and prepared for the big day. The church is in this stage now. Christ is preparing His bride to be with Him throughout eternity by "cleansing her by the washing of water through the word". He has already dealt with His people's guilt in making her "holy", but He goes on cleansing her from the power and pollution of sin as she waits for the day of His coming.

d) Wedding: When Christ returns for His bride, He will "present her to Himself as a radiant church, without stain or wrinkle or any other blemish". This does not make Christ's return dependent on a perfect church, but it indicates that there will be a beautiful, faithful bride on the earth at His coming. Then He will give His bride her wedding dress — glorious perfection — and the church will process amid great rejoicing to be joined to her beloved Saviour for ever. Complete Revelation 19:6-9 below.

"Then I heard what sounded like a great multitude, like the roar of rushing waters and like loud peals of thunder, shouting:

....

....

....

....

....

....

.... "

"Then the angel said to me, 'Write: "Blessed are those who are invited to the wedding supper of the Lamb!"' And he added, 'These are the true words of God.'"

Covenant Love in Marriage

This message of Christ's love for His bride, the church, is at the heart of Paul's practical teaching to husbands and wives. Marriage could hardly have been given any greater honour than to be used in such a glorious picture and comparison.

Look through Ephesians 5:22-33 again. What specific instructions for married men and women can you find in them? Write anything you identify in the right-hand column, and in the centre column write which truth about Christ and the Church corresponds with it. Do this together as a couple (or as a group).

Eph 5	Christ & the Church	Husband & Wife
verses 22-24		
verses 25-27		
verses 28-32		

Two vital words require closer attention at this point. Both are essential for the working out of covenant love in marriage, and each has Jesus Christ as its perfect example.

The first is "submit" and the second is the word "love" itself.

a) "Wives submit to your husbands"
The call to "submit" is addressed to the wife. "As the church submits to Christ, so also wives should submit to their husbands in everything". The word "submit" has a military background, describing the authority of one rank in relation to another. In due course it came to be used more generally of "yielding the place of importance to another".

The apostle Paul, writing against a background of the brutal subjection of numerous sections of society, describes a very different kind of submission.

Firstly, it is voluntary. Wives are to submit *themselves* (See the King James translation). In fact, submission ceases to be Christian when it is enforced by tyranny or coerced by fear. Many wives in Paul's day had little outward choice about submission (they were their husband's property!). But each had a choice about submitting from the heart. So do you.

Look up the following passages of Scripture. What do they say to you about a woman's voluntary submission to her husband?

Titus 2:4,5

....
....
....

....

....

....

The woman portrayed in these two Scriptures could not be further removed from the caricature of the nagging wife in the book of Proverbs. Look up 19:13b and 25:24. If you can smile together at the description, all is well. If, however, it is too close for comfort, reach for your ladder!

What does this mean for your marriage? Talk together as a couple about these expressions of a wife's submission to her husband. How can they be worked out in practice?

* "I will look to you for spiritual headship in our marriage." (1 Cor 11:3)
* "I want you to be manager of the team." (1 Tim 3:4)
* "I will always honour and esteem you." (Eph 5:33)

Secondly, submission is Godward. Write below each reference to God in Paul's teaching about a wife's submission.

"Wives submit to your husbands

...." (Eph 5:22)

"Wives submit to your husbands

...." (Col 3:18)

When you yield to your husband it is an expression of your submission to God. In fact, this is a principle which applies to every kind of Christian submission, whether by a man or woman:

* parents and children in the home (Eph 6:1-4)
* elders and people in the church (Heb 13:17)
* bosses and staff in the workplace (Col 3:22-24)
* authorities and citizens in the nation (Rom 13:1-7)

Write out Ephesians 5:21. These words cover every kind of submission in or out of marriage.

"...

...."

This time "reverence for Christ" is in view. He is, after all, the supreme example of voluntary, Godward submission. When you submit, you are being a disciple of Jesus.
Write out Philippians 2:5-7.

"...

....

....

....

....

...."

b) "Husbands, love your wives"
If "submit" is a key word for a wife, then "love" is the equivalent for a husband. Once again, the apostle emphasises a radically different view of headship and submission. Whereas the norm in his day was for a husband to demand submission, Paul writes of a husband winning submission by his love for his wife.

Many husbands still need to grasp this. Some men want to rule the roost and tend to be somewhat selfish and careless in their relationship with their wife. Others are happy to muddle in and tend to be indecisive and indifferent towards her. A wife will respond best not to coercion nor to passivity but to love. Husbands, love your wives!

The word used in the New Testament to describe this "love" is "agape". It conveys a Godlike love which is sacrificial, unconditional, permanent and demonstrated in action. It is a love rooted in the will rather than emotion. Jesus exemplified "agape" love, and called His disciples to do the same.

"..

....

...." (John 13:34)

This is the kind of love every marriage needs, in both husband and wife! However, the apostle emphasises, "*husbands* love your wives, just as Christ loved the church and gave Himself up for her". How does this work in practice? Look through the following list. Each statement emphasises that "agape" love is a decision, rooted in the will rather than the emotions. Having read them, think of some down-to-earth examples in typical situations in your marriage.

1. I will demonstrate my love for you by actions, and not just by words.

....

....

....

2. I will show my love for you despite any personal inconvenience it involves.

....

....

....

3. I will give you my love unconditionally rather than on the basis of your behaviour, performance or attitude to me.

....

....

....

4. I will demonstrate the permanence of my love for you by faithfulness and loyalty.

....

....

....

5. I will not withhold love in order to punish, express hurt or show my disapproval of you.

....

....

....

6. I will be consistent in my love for you, rather than alternate according to my mood or circumstances.

....

....

....

7. I will be constructive and practical in my love for you.

....

....

....

8. I will not wait for you to change before seeking to love you more.

....

....

....

9. I will take the initiative in showing you love.

....

....

....

10. I will seek to love you in ways best suited to your well-being.

....

....

....

11. I will affirm and build you up rather than heap a sense of failure
    or guilt upon you.

....

....

....

12. I will never deliberately give you a reason to feel insecure by my
    attitudes, actions or words.

....

....

....

13. I will love you by thinking of your interests rather than my rights.

....

....

....

14. I will love you even though it means sacrifice, even that of my life.

....

....

....

No one can feel smug after reading such a list! In fact every husband reading this should, by now, be on his knees before God! That is exactly what is needed. "Agape" love does not come naturally to us! To be able to love like this we need help and resources beyond our own powers of will and determination. Only when Jesus' life flows through us can we love others with His perfect love.

Write out John 15:5.

"..

....

...."

To be able to love like this we also need to know that we are loved in the same way.

Write out John 15:9.

"..

....

...."

Husbands, you need to "be strong in the grace that is in Christ Jesus" (2 Tim 2:1) as you seek to love your wife. There will be times when you fall short, and others when you feel a total failure. Don't give up. Return to "the throne of grace with confidence to receive mercy and find grace to help" (Heb 4:16).

Wives, you too need God's grace to encourage your husband as he reaches out in love to you. From that place of being loved, your own love for him will develop and flourish.

To close this chapter, here is an exercise which should be illuminating and fun at the same time. Compose your own amplified version of 1 Corinthians 13:4-8 below. Do it together as a couple, agreeing on suitable additions (even including names when appropriate). An example in our case could be, "Love is patient when John puts off mending the shed". Or "Love is not easily angered even when Liz has given one of my favourite suits to Oxfam".

"Love is patient

....

Love is kind

....

It does not envy

....

It does not boast

....

It is not proud

....

It is not rude

....

It is not self-seeking

....

It is not easily angered

....

It keeps no record of wrongs

....

Love does not delight in evil but rejoices with the truth.
It always protects

....

Always trusts

....

Always hopes

....

Always perseveres

....

Love never fails."

....

Having done this, read it out together. What you have prepared should read much more like a Covenant than a Contract. By living in such Covenant love together you will be *Honouring Marriage*.

Assignment
Look at Appendix 2, "Reaffirming your Marriage Covenant". Arrange an appropriate time and setting to use this. If your Wedding Anniversary is imminent, that would be an ideal opportunity.

Chapter 4 LEARNING TO COMMUNICATE

Good communication is essential if there is to be growing trust and closeness between husband and wife. Lack of communication is at the heart of the majority of marital problems.

Tens of thousands of couples endure a sub-standard existence under the same roof instead of a warm, loving marriage, because this ingredient is missing. Others go through unnecessary tensions and traumas, some of which lead to the breakup of the marriage itself.

Even the most intelligent of men and women can display appalling ignorance and ineptitude when it comes to knowing how to keep the channels of communication open between them.

This lesson, which largely takes the form of a self-assessment exercise, aims to help you think about communication in your marriage.

Even those of you who are good at keeping in touch with each other's lives should learn something which will improve your sharing.

Levels of Communication
There are different levels of communication, some superficial and others intimate, some safe and others risky. Every level has its place.

Those who always want to relate at depth can be draining and those who trot out clichés can be boring.

Look at the levels of communication listed below. Think of an example of each of them. They have not been listed in any particular order.

hopes/dreams
ideas
feelings
information/practicalities
vision/faith

reminiscences
opinions/convictions
clichés
personal advice or correction
banter (humour)

Now look at the diagram of the swimming pool and write down at what depth you would you put each of these ten different levels of communication.

Shallow End   Deep End

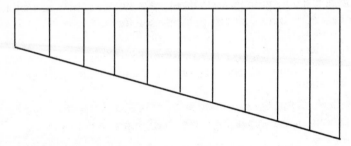

The swimming-pool metaphor is worth staying with for a little while longer. Talk together about the following statements — with communication in mind.

(i)   The shallow end helps you get used to the water.
(ii) The whole pool is there to be used.
(iii) One person's shallow end may be too deep for another.
(iv) The pool is intended as much for enjoyment as it is for serious swimming.
(v)   The mature swimmer does not want to stay at the shallow end.
(vi) The deep end needs to be treated with caution.

Ways of Communicating
How do we go about communicating?

The following different ways of communicating should be familiar to you. Work through each of the sections assessing yourself honestly. Be prepared to share personal responses with your partner when you have completed the exercise.

a) Communicating by speech
Conversation is a missing ingredient in many marriages. Wives, in particular, express disappointment over their husband's inability or unwillingness to communicate. Before marriage the two were able to talk freely, but now there doesn't seem to be much communicating going on.

Is this true of your marriage? For example, do you sit down and talk to one another? How often? Many couples come up against a variety of barriers to the simplest forms of communication. Here are a few such barriers. Are any of them a hindrance to you?

☐ television	home computer
☐ radio	reading
☐ music	work brought home
☐ children	no time to relax
☐ tiredness	unresolved problems
☐ silent rut	personality clash
☐ nothing to talk about	I'm the silent type
☐ telephone	unresponsive partner
☐ I can't get a word in!	others:

....

....

....

Having looked at these negatives move on now to some positive statements, each of which demonstrates how to communicate by speech. Give yourself a rating on a scale of 1-10 below (1 — poor, 10 — excellent)

.... I tell my partner all about my day.

.... I remember to pass on information, messages and news.

.... I listen attentively, rather than interrupt or dominate conversation.

.... I share my worries, hurts, needs, joys and frustrations with my partner.

.... I recognise how my partner is feeling behind the words he/she uses.

.... I am able to face difficulties and sensitive issues with my partner.

.... I talk about what I believe.

.... I share my hopes, dreams and ideas.

.... I am able to express my opinions without being aggressive or blinkered.

.... I can talk freely about my childhood and early years.

.... I am open to discussing any aspect of my life — there are no "no-go" areas.

.... I am alert to speak positive words to my partner: eg "thank you"; "well done"; "I love you"; "I understand"; "I'm proud of you"; "You look great"; "I love being with you".

.... I communicate trust in God by what I say.

.... I am conscious not only of what I say, but the way I say it.

b) Communicating in writing

Some who find it difficult to express themselves in speech are transformed into excellent communicators when a pen is put into their hand. Are you, or have you ever been, in the habit of writing to one another? You may have written letters, picture cards, surprise notes, or even poetry!

Why not plan to leave a loving note or card for your spouse in an unexpected place sometime during this coming week? You might even decide that it is an excellent habit to develop, and end up with an album full!

On our Marriage Courses couples have excelled at this, and had great fun in the process. Loving notes have turned up in sandwiches, under toilet seats, stretched across bedrooms on banners and so on.

One mischievous wife sent her message in a box to her husband's office. When he opened it (watched by his colleagues) a red heart-shaped helium-filled balloon floated to the ceiling declaring the message, "I love you!"

Another husband had some explaining to do when his colleagues at work read his wife's loving telegram before he did. They would not believe it was from his wife! They were sure he must be having an affair. This indicates just how important it is for us to go on being innovative as husband and wife. Demonstrate to those around you that there is, despite the cynicism, "life after marriage"!

Try writing a loving note to each other in the next ten minutes. Exchange your notes later and enjoy what your partner has written. Don't strain to write as much as you can in the time allotted! Quality rather than quantity is the target to aim for.

c) Communicating with the eyes

For a man and a woman, so much can be communicated in this way. Look up these verses in the Song of Songs:

4:9
"You have stolen my heart, my sister, my bride. You have stolen my heart with...

....

...."

6:5
"Turn...

....,

....they overwhelm me"

What do you think such glances were communicating?

....

....

....

It is not only passion that is communicated by the eye! Talk together about the different messages conveyed by the following:

Smiles

....

Eye contact

....

Noticing how each other looks

....

Being comfortable in silence together

....

Looking at each other when the other is speaking

....

Now check out your eye communication with one another by rating yourselves on each using a scale of 1-5.

It may seem to be stating the obvious, but facial expressions and eye communication need to match the tone and content of what you say. A husband may whisper, "I love you" to his wife in the most seductive tone, but if his eyes are fixed on the Nine O'Clock News, she is unlikely to be impressed! A wife may praise her husband's valiant attempt at carpentry, but if her expression says, "Am I expected to sit on it or hang it on the wall?", he may need urgent consolation.

d) Communicating by touch
From sight we turn to touch, and specifically non-sexual touch. Turn to the following two Scriptures, both of which portray Jesus communicating in this way.

Mark 1:41,42

"Filled...

.... 'I am willing,' He said. 'Be clean!' Immediately the leprosy left him, and he was cured."

Mark 10:13
"People were bringing children to Jesus to.....................................

...."

Now for a bit of fun! Sit close together as a couple and take turns to communicate some of the following to your partner without using words. Giggling *is* allowed! You need not be restricted to the hands during this exercise; there are other ways of communicating by touch, eg head on shoulder, kiss on cheek, nudge with a knee!

If you are part of a group do please make sure you are not squeezing someone else's spouse! Your group leader can read out the words, as well as keep an eye on you all! Here goes:

comfort	secret message
affection	belonging
fun and games	reassurance
encouragement	admiration

Communicating by touch is more than a silly game. Holding hands when you are out walking, an arm around a shoulder, and hugs and cuddles all convey love and closeness to your partner. There will be times when words are inadequate but taking your husband's or your wife's hands in yours will say all that needs to be said.

e) Communicating by actions

Read John 13:1-5 together. Jesus' act of lowly service was a powerful means of communication. His action spoke louder than words.

This is Liz's perspective. "Big acts of kindness are very nice, but just as meaningful to me are the little things. For instance, when John says, 'Sit down and I'll bring you a cup of coffee' or 'I'll photocopy those teaching notes for you' or when he goes out of his way to help with supermarket expeditions."

As a couple or group, identify practical examples of letting actions speak. Think of specific ways of putting each of the four words in the table below into action (and make sure you go on to do them sometime!)

Courtesy	Unselfishness
Loyalty	Thoughtfulness

As you turn the pages to each new chapter you will see that Communication is at the heart of this book. This is particularly true of the exercises and assignments, most of which encourage you to express yourselves to one another.

Sometimes you may find the process difficult and, perhaps, even painful. Please don't yield to the temptation to withdraw from it. Very often the most important moments of discovery and understanding take place between you when you feel vulnerable. You will learn skills and develop a style of your own as you communicate. No two couples are the same.

That is why books, and the advice or example of others, though valuable, can never present you with the definitive formula for communication. You need to discover what works for you.

Here are a few of the personal lessons we have learned.

1. Communication on a deep level needs to be given sufficient time with as little interruption as possible.

2. Reassurance and encouragement are important when communicating at depth.

3. It is easy to neglect communication — eg John: "I usually wanted to leave my day behind, but Liz needed to know about it. If she drew me I would try to give as brief a report as possible, when she wanted more detail."

4. There are helpful ways of spending time together which give an opportunity for communication to take place. For example:
   with a cup of tea in bed
   going for a walk
   meals together (in or out)
   driving
   working in the garden together
   The best of all has proved to be prayer times together.

5. There are also times to avoid — eg when too tired, or distracted (a veiled reference to the "Big Match"!)

6. Confidentiality is crucial.

7. Don't push too hard if certain subjects are very sensitive. It is better to approach it little by little than to dive headlong into the deep end and nearly drown!

8. Like many marriages, we have come up against male reluctance to express emotions! Liz writes, "John had a tendency to bury his worries and fears. He has slowly learned to share them, and I know

that it has helped him to feel that I understand and care. It always makes me feel valued and trusted when he can be open with me."

Can you now do the same? Compile your own list.

Assignment
Compare and talk together about each other's self-assessment. Agree on how you will attempt to improve your communication with each other.

Chapter 5   PRAYING TOGETHER

The subject of praying together is usually near the top of the list when Christian couples talk about their failures and frustrations in marriage. Very few deny the importance of prayer, and yet most husbands and wives feel defeated and ashamed when it is mentioned.

But is it really that important? Sometimes praying together is perceived as a duty: one of those unspoken "musts" for Christian marriage. Only rarely is it seen for what it really is — one of the most important keys to intimacy between man and wife.

Some couples have experienced this. For them, prayer has provided the ideal setting to share their deepest feelings with one another as well as God. A transparency and trust has been possible that is reminiscent of Adam and Eve in the Garden before sin's consequences came between them.

Look up Genesis 2:25 and complete below:

"The man and his wife...

...."

Emotional "nakedness" without any fear of criticism or scorn, is possible when you draw near to God together. Here in His presence, more than anywhere else, you can express your innermost convictions, doubts and feelings, and this deep sharing binds you together.

In Ecclesiastes 4:9-12 you will find an enigmatic reference to this kind of bond. Having portrayed a relationship between two people in terms of partnership and companionship, the writer suddenly adds an unexpected note.

Write out the last sentence of verse 12 below.

"..

...."

What do you make of this "cord of three strands"?

....

....

....

For a couple whose lives are intertwined with the Lord Jesus Christ, He is the third, and the strongest, cord. In the words of Cliff Richard's song, it is "You and me and Jesus".

You — and Jesus
Before going any further, however, you need to look at your personal relationship with Christ. Do you spend time in prayer alone? Have you built into your life a regular pattern of personal prayer and enjoyment of God's Word? If not, this could be why you have sometimes struggled with praying together.

You cannot make prayer with your partner a substitute for drawing near to God yourself. When this happens, husbands and wives almost always fail to sustain praying together because they meet each other with little to give.

Consult the following Scriptures and write down below any practical pointers for private prayer that you can find: Daniel 6:10; Matthew 6:5-15; Mark 1:35.

1..

2..

3..

4...

5...

6...

Now look at your list with an eye to any specific adjustments you may need to make in your personal praying. Talk them over with your partner. Ask your husband/wife to help you follow through any decisions you make.

Your personal time with the Lord will overflow into the time you spend together in prayer as a couple. Here are three simple suggestions to help you forge the link between the two.

a) Seek something encouraging about *God* from the Scriptures to share with your partner each day. Read any relevant passage from the Bible to him/her.
b) Pray for your *partner's* needs and ask the Lord to show you ways of ministering His love to your partner each day. Thank God for your husband/wife, focusing on the qualities you appreciate most.
c) Talk through with your partner anything God has shown you about *yourself*.

Lessons from the Past
(i) Past failures do not disqualify you from trying to pray together again. In fact, the lessons you can learn should help you considerably. Take a look at the following selection of hazards and tick any that you identify with:

❏ embarrassment   too shy or self-conscious
❏ apathy   indifference, laziness, "can't be bothered"
❏ indiscipline   intentions 100%, follow-through 0%
❏ irritations   tone of voice, length of prayers, domination
❏ insecurity   don't feel spiritual enough, afraid to open up

❑ predictability   very boring and routine
❑ others   ....

                     ....

                     ....

As you look over this list, ask these questions together:

* Have we ever admitted this to one another before?
* Why did these things become such a problem?
* How can we prevent this happening again in the future?

(ii) Have your reasons for wanting to pray together been healthy?
Below you will find a collection of different motivations, some
much better than others. Look through them and tick those which
are in line with the Scriptures referred to.

❑ I want to worship and enjoy God with my partner (Eph 5:19,20)
❑ I want to get my partner sorted out (Eph 5:33)
❑ I want to help build up my partner in her/his faith in Christ
(Col 3:16,17)
❑ I want to feel less guilty when prayer is mentioned (Rom 8:1)
❑ I want our marriage to be an effective prayer unit
(Matt 18:18-20)
❑ I want to come closer to Christ with my partner so that our love
for one another is deepened (John 15:9-12)

Check your response by turning to Appendix 1.

(iii) Changed circumstances need to be taken into account. The pattern
of prayer which suited you so perfectly as newly-weds is unlikely
to work if you now have four children under the age of six! You
need flexibility to be able to adapt to whatever changes come your
way.

How have you adjusted to your changed circumstances in married life so far? Which adjustments were successes and which were flops? Call a few examples to mind briefly and mention them to each other.

Bearing in mind your present circumstances, what is the most realistic arrangement for praying together now? Talk through the following questions before writing anything down.

1. When is the best time for us to pray together?

....

2. How long could we spend?

    Shortest time ....

    Longest time................................

3. How often can we do this?

....

4. Where is the best place to pray together?

....

5. What are likely to be the main pressures upon us?

....

6. When shall we start?

....

The Way Forward

On some days it will only be possible for you to pray together briefly. This makes it all the more important to set aside quality time in your family schedule so that you can draw near to God in an unhurried way. This will open up many new dimensions in the adventure of praying as husband and wife.

As you embark on any new strategy of praying together, give some careful thought to the following:

* the Bible
* the Holy Spirit
* worship
* ministering to each other
* calling on God together
* variety

a) The Bible
This is the best springboard to prayer. You may find it helpful to have a plan of action so that God's Word has a regular place in your time together. Are any of the following ideas of use to you, and can you add others of your own?

❑ Read a book of the Bible through in stages.
❑ Read a Psalm and a New Testament passage.
❑ Concentrate on a theme or doctrine for a period.
❑ Use daily reading notes (a variety are available).
❑ Use another of this "How to" series when you have completed this one.
❑ Use specific passages (eg the Lord's Prayer).
❑ Explore biblical meditation together (Campbell MacAlpine's *The Practice of Biblical Meditation* is well worth reading).

Have you had some difficulty in the past when attempting to combine prayer with Bible reading? If so, talk about it together. Learn the lessons of the past and find a formula that suits you.

b) The Holy Spirit
God has given you the Holy Spirit to help you pray! Write out Romans 8:26:

"...

....
....
....
...."

The Spirit is sometimes called the "Paraclete" or "Comforter". This literally means that He "comes alongside to help". He is able to transform your time together from a formal "saying your prayers" to a dynamic time of revelation because, as the Spirit of God, He knows the mind of God.

Read 1 Corinthians 2:9-16 and write out verses 12 and 13 below.

"...
....
....
....
....
....
...."

Are there ways in which the gifts of the Holy Spirit may be sought or stirred up in your praying together? (See Romans 12:3-8 and 1 Cor 12:4-11).

If you have never sought or received the baptism in the Holy Spirit, now may be the time! Read the following Scriptures and, as they build faith in you, ask the Lord to fill you with the Spirit. It may be appropriate to pray for your partner, or let your partner pray for you. If you are part of a group, pray for one another. (John 1:29-34; 4:4-15; Luke 11:9-13; Acts 1:4,5,8; 2:1-4; 19:1-7)

c) Worship

What about worship? For some, this is synonymous with music and singing. Many who are tone deaf or clap out of time shrink with embarrassment at the very thought of worshipping as a twosome!

Of course, some of you may be into singing the latest (or even your own) worship songs accompanied by a guitar. Many of us envy you! But who says that praise and worship must be set to music?

The worship of heaven is often "said" not "sung"! Take a look at Revelation 4:8,10; 11:15-17. Sometimes it is "shouted"! (19:1-8).

Music and singing do undoubtedly aid us in worship. Why not play worship cassettes? Have the volume low enough for the sound not to intrude when you are praying, but loud enough to sing along with if you wish.

Expect God to break into your times together so that you sing and shout out your praise, and whisper your adoration and love to Him.

d) Ministering to each other

Give yourselves time to minister to each other's needs. This will not be possible at length or in depth every time you pray together, but you should consider setting time aside sometimes for this to happen. It usually requires unhurried quality time to make you feel ready to "open up" with one another. If you, or your partner, are tired or fretting over the clock, or afraid of interruptions — forget it!

Sensitivity is also needed. Don't assume that your partner is automatically eager to become vulnerable by sharing their anxieties, anger, disappointments and inadequacies. By blundering in you can set back intimate sharing rather than develop it.

Can you add other suggestions to the following list of ways to minister the love of Jesus to your spouse?

72

* Listen attentively, with understanding.
* Affirm your love and respect.
* Offer to pray for him/her.
* Speak out a blessing upon your partner in the name of Jesus.

* ....

* ....

* ....

e) Calling on God together

You Honour Marriage when you draw near to God together with "all kinds of prayers and requests" (Eph 6:18). You are raising it above an earth-bound state of unbelief to the throne room of the King of Kings! You are also forging yourselves into a vital prayer unit.

Read Matthew 18:18-20 again and write out verse 19 below.

" ....
....
....
...."

What a promise! No wonder Satan makes it his aim to rob couples of their joy in praying together! He knows what devastation they can cause to his dominion of darkness when they cry out in faith to God in the name of Jesus!

Have some clear outward-looking content to your praying. This prevents your time together from becoming intense and introspective. Check out the following list of important prayer targets, adding others to the list. On a separate piece of paper write specific names and details alongside the subjects.

- ❏ family
- ❏ friends
- ❏ workmates
- ❏ neighbours
- ❏ church leaders
- ❏ church ministries
- ❏ international issues
- ❏ local issues
- ❏ national issues
- ❏ overseas mission

You will know the joy of seeing your prayers answered as you call on God together. However, the apostle Peter sounded a note of warning in his first letter. What did he suggest might be a setback to your prayers?

Look up 1 Peter 3:7 and put it in your own words.

....

....

....

.

f) Variety

Inject variety into your time together. Praying as husband and wife can be either a highlight or a bore! Keep talking about how you feel about your times of prayer to make sure they stay fresh and stimulating. Here are a few lighthearted questions to ask yourselves:

1. Do fun and laughter have any place in your times of praying together?

....

2. When did you last steal and incorporate a good idea from another couple? What was it?

....

3. Who always starts your times of prayer?

....

4. Who has a tendency to sermonise?

....

5. What jargon or religious language does each of you lapse into?

....

6. Imitate a religious tone of voice. Does it sound anything like your voice when you pray?

....

7. Do you adopt a head-in-hands position when you pray? Why/Why not?

....

8. Have you ever fallen asleep during a time of prayer?

....

9. How many different places have you used to pray together — indoors and outdoors? Recall them.

....

As this chapter closes, take a look at the following four case studies. In each the couple is experiencing difficulty praying together. Talk about each case, looking carefully at the information you are given. Ask, "What are the real reasons for their difficulty?" "How can their situation be changed for the better?" Be as specific and practical as possible. As you discuss these cases (especially in a group) be alert for anything that fits your needs.

Case Studies

1. Jim and Sally

Jim and Sally have been married for eighteen months and have both known the Lord for about six years. Jim is a civil servant; he works in London, catching the 7.30 train each morning, and returning home by

6.45 p.m. Sally is eight months' pregnant, and so no longer works as a dentist's receptionist.

Sally is disappointed that Jim doesn't take the initiative about them praying together. When she has expressed her frustration, Jim has responded, and they have prayed together each day for half an hour or more before the old pattern has taken over again.

Jim feels guilty. Although Sally prays by herself and with a few friends, he rarely spends time alone with God and has lost contact with his friends. He does make it to the church prayer meeting most weeks. Sally doesn't like to say anything to her friends or pastor because it would feel like a betrayal of her husband, but she knows something needs to change. She expected praying together to be an important part of Christian marriage, and wants Jim to be a strong spiritual head in their family. She remembers how her mother and father prayed and read their Bible every evening for half an hour before going to bed, and longs for the same in her marriage.

2. Trevor and Jane

From day one there has been no regular pattern of praying together for Trevor and Jane. They have been married for three years, and do not have any children (although they hope to start a family in two years' time). Trevor is a policeman and Jane is a social worker. Both work unpredictable hours; Trevor often has shift work while Jane may have evening visits or be on emergency "stand-by". Each has made a positive impact as a Christian in their sphere of work. Sometimes however, it feels as if they are not married at all!

They usually manage to make it to Sunday worship together once a fortnight, but regular attendance at housegroup is impossible. Trevor and Jane pray as individuals but neither has a great sense of needing to pray together regularly.

3. Michael and Judy

Michael and Judy have been married for seven years. They have three children: Stephen (6), Peter (4 — and hyperactive) and Rachel (14 months).

Michael has been baptised in the Holy Spirit recently, and is enjoying the gift of tongues in his own times of prayer. His spiritual life has been transformed! Judy is pleased about the new vitality in Michael's life. She too loves the Lord. Some years ago she was baptised in the Spirit, but the pressures of coping with the children have made her weary. It is a long time now since she last "felt" God's love or His presence.

At present her chief pressure is baby Rachel's sleeping pattern — or lack of it! The little darling requires Mummy at least twice during the night, and sometimes Judy feels as if she has not slept at all. Michael is a deep sleeper, and anyway he has a demanding job which requires him to be fresh for work each day. He helps with the children when he returns home at 6.30 p.m. It seems ages to Judy since they had a meal out together — just the two of them.

They pray together sometimes at the end of the day, but it is not a great success because of tiredness. Once a week they have just begun to set aside an evening to talk and pray together. Judy is already finding these evenings a threat and is beginning to dread them. Michael senses her nervousness but is sure that God is going to renew her spiritual life in the same way as his own. He would like to pray over her for this, but she has asked him not to.

4. Bill and Betty

Bill and Betty are bored with their prayer times together, but neither has admitted it to the other. For twenty-four years they have woken at 6.30 a.m., made two cups of tea in the "Teasmade" before reading their Daily Bible Study notes and praying together until 7.00 a.m.

Bill prays one long prayer first; Betty timed a particularly long one at seventeen and a half minutes. With rare exceptions, he begins with thanks to God for salvation and His "many blessings", and then proceeds to pray for the elders of the church, the Prime Minister, Royal Family and missionary work in Zaire and the Dominican Republic. He closes with thanks to God for Betty.

Betty prays for Bill and their married son, his wife and the two grandchildren. She does so in a very quiet voice which Bill has difficulty in hearing (and which is a source of secret irritation to him). They believe that praying together is the backbone of married life. After all, as Bill likes to say, "the couple that prays together, stays together".

Assignment
Agree on a timetable for praying together over the next week. Don't bite off more than you can chew! Review it at the end of the week and then plan towards the next week.

Chapter 6 FAMILY CONNECTIONS

This chapter is more suitable for you to tackle as a couple in the privacy of your own home than with a group because the subject matter is so personal.

Before you proceed any further, have your family photograph albums close at hand. Why not go and search them out right now? Don't forget to include old photos of grandma and grandad as well as childhood pictures of yourselves with your parents and brothers and sisters.

Before thinking specifically of your "Family Connections" take a look at a Biblical character. Open your Bible around Genesis 12.

Isaac and His Family
Everyone is affected by their family background. Many of your attitudes and personal traits will reflect your upbringing and different relationships (or lack of them) in your early years.

Think about Isaac in this light, using the Scriptures to explore these questions.
What do you know about Isaac's parents?
Gen 11:27-31; 12:1-5; 12:10-20

....

....

....

What were the circumstances of Isaac's birth? Do you think he would have been loved and cared for as a child?
Gen 15:1-6; 18:10-15; 21:1-7

....

....

....

What effect might the following childhood incidents have had upon Isaac?
Gen 21:8-14; 22:1-19

....

....

....

What "Family Connections" were involved in Isaac's marriage?
Gen 24

....

....

....

What characteristics of his father can you detect in Isaac in his mature years?
Gen 25:19-28; 26:1-11

....

....

....

You and Your History
What memories do you have of your early years? Taking turns, use your family photographs to talk to each other about your childhood years. Reminisce about your grandparents, mum and dad, brothers

and sisters. How well did you relate to them? Describe your home, your bedroom, any memorable holidays, house moves, and any outstanding memories from your schooldays. What about special friends and childhood games or toys?

Listen lovingly to your partner, particularly when he/she shares something intimate. Try not to interrupt, except to clarify any detail when necessary.

If photographs are hard to come by, here is a different exercise. Find a large sheet of paper and divide it into three sections (as below). Now, in each section draw anything that springs to mind in the years specified. Don't restrict yourself to momentous events; include silly little memories as well.

Keep your drawings simple (eg use "stick" men and women). The object of the exercise is not to produce an artistic masterpiece, but to recall impressions and memories of your childhood.

0-5 years	13-16 years
6-12 years	

Take some time now to show your partner what you have drawn. Explain any detail and try to remember how you felt about any incident or relationship. What does your picture tell you about your childhood? How might those early years have affected you in marriage?

Having listened to each other, can you see any similarities in your background? Did your families function in similar ways and share the same values? How well would your partner have fitted into your family — as a brother or sister?

List any similarities

....

....

....

What about differences?

....

....

....

Your childhood and family background have made a major contribution to the person you are today, and to your marriage. Knowing this can help you to understand the way you relate to one another, and also identify areas of your life where you need God to make you whole.

Here are some very personal questions to talk over together. Each focuses on an important stage of emotional development in your early years. It is almost certain that these questions will (a) touch sensitive issues causing some emotion to surface, and (b) reveal gaps or deficiencies in some stages of your development. Take encouragement from the knowledge that you are not a rare exception; nor are you a prisoner of your past, because you are now a new creation in Christ (2 Cor 5:17).

Write out 1 Peter 1:3,4 before you think about the questions that follow.

" ....
....
....
....
....
....
.... "

* To what extent were you loved and cared for as a baby?
Your mother had a special role at this important stage. When you are sure that you are loved, you are secure enough to love others; that includes your partner and your children.

* How much loving discipline did you receive as a child?
What part did your father play in this? When you have experienced consistent, loving authority and control you are in a better position to accept and exert it yourself in adulthood — including marriage.

* How well did you mix with other children in your early years?
Through play and the ups and downs of friendships, rivalries, and the need to share, you learn how to relate to others.

* What sort of contact did you have with the opposite sex as you grew up?
Brothers and sisters, or boys and girls at school or in a church help prepare you for mature relationships with the opposite sex.

* What model of marriage did you have in your home?
The example of your parents' relationship influences your hopes and expectations for marriage — for better or worse!

* How did you begin to exert your independence in the teen years?
When you cease clinging to your parents and begin to find support and identity in others' company, this prepares you for leaving your father and mother, and cleaving to your partner.

You will probably find it helpful to pray for each other at this point, especially if some area of sensitivity has been touched. Remember, Jesus Christ is the answer to your deepest needs.

Read Hebrews 4:14-16 and write out verse 16 before going on to pray for each other.

"...

....

...."

If these questions have made you feel totally out of your depth, then it would be wise for you to consult your pastor, or another experienced counsellor or friend.

This is particularly important in the event of a previously buried memory of parental abuse being uncovered, or some other serious trauma.

Relations with your Relations
Marriage involved the "leaving" of your father and mother. This did not mean that you cut them out of your life, but that your relationship with them needed to change.

What about your experience of "leaving"? How are your relations with your relations? Use the following checklist to help you think more deeply about this.

We found "leaving" difficult.	YES/NO
We enjoy visiting our parents.	YES/NO/SOMETIMES
We enjoy visits by our parents.	YES/NO/SOMETIMES
Our parents are intimidating.	YES/NO
Our parents are possessive.	YES/NO
Our parents are supportive.	YES/NO
Our parents are manipulative.	YES/NO
Our parents are thoughtful.	YES/NO
Our parents are interfering.	YES/NO
We rely on them too much.	YES/NO
We criticise each other to them.	YES/NO/SOMETIMES
We allow parental interference to divide us.	YES/NO/SOMETIMES
Mother (Mother-in-law) and daughter relationships are harmonious.	YES/NO
We have some "No go" areas with them.	YES/NO

If YES, what are they?

....

We have had problems with other members of our family	YES/NO

In some cases, newly-weds may be prevented from establishing themselves because of parental interference. David and Michal faced this to a degree that few reading this will encounter! (1 Sam 18:12-29; 19:8-17). King Saul's fear and jealousy did not allow the young couple to grow together as husband and wife.

Has parental domination been a problem for you? On one occasion we asked a question like this of a married couple and they answered immediately and in unison. The only trouble was that the wife said,

"Yes" and the husband, "No"!

Of course it would be misleading to suggest that the parents are always at fault. Sometimes one of the newly-weds is reluctant to "let go", causing tension and strife with their partner.

When you learn to work out two complementary Biblical principles you should be able to enjoy excellent relations with your father and mother. You will find these principles in the following two passages. Write out the verses below and underline the key phrase in each.

"...
....
...." (Gen 2:24)

"...
....
...." (Ex 20:12)

Firstly, what does it mean to "*leave*" your father and mother? Look through the following statements and indicate which of them is a true application of the Biblical principle.

❏ Our parents' authority over us has ceased.
❏ We should not set up home with them.
❏ We need to be allowed to build a life of our own.
❏ Their responsibility for us has come to an end.
❏ We should not expect them to keep "bailing us out" of financial difficulties.
❏ We should be able to take or leave their advice.
❏ They must allow us to resolve our conflicts without interfering.

Turn to Appendix 1 for a brief comment on these statements.

Now look back over these seven statements. If you agree with them as principles, what about in practice? Talk about anything you need to attend to in order to create healthier relations with your relations.

Secondly, what does it mean to *"honour"* your father and mother? The Bible gives us some good models. Look up the following scriptures. How did these people honour their parents and in-laws? Summarise each example in a sentence.

Moses (Ex 18:7,8)

....

....

....

Boaz and Ruth (Ruth 4:13-17)

....

....

....

David (1 Sam 24)

....

....

....

Simon Peter (Mark 1:29-31)

....

....

....

The Lord Jesus Christ (John 19:25-27; cf 1 Tim 5:4)

....

....

....

Assignment
Write down six practical ways in which you can express love and esteem to your parents over the next year. Decide how and when you will do these things.

1..

2..

3..

4..

5..

6..

Are there any unresolved difficulties between you and any members of your or your partner's family? Determine now to go the extra mile in seeking or giving forgiveness where it is needed. So many people live with guilt after their parents' death because they were too proud or stubborn to restore a relationship.

As a couple, set aside some time to pray at length for the different members of your family with their various circumstances and needs. Pray particularly for any who may still not know Christ for themselves.

Chapter 7 UNDERSTANDING ONE ANOTHER

Everyone is unique. A "once in the history of the universe" combination of factors has made you who you are with your distinctive character, physical appearance, personality, temperament and so on. You even have a unique genetic "fingerprint" to prove it.

All this makes you very special. You are more than a valuable limited edition; you are a priceless "one-off".

However, because you are unique, you are also complex, so much so that you can never fully understand yourself. In fact, the Bible teaches that only God Himself really knows you. In Psalm 139 David meditates on this. Read his words and then write out the verses below.

"..
...."(v.1)
"..
....
....
....
...." (vv.13,14)
"..
....
....
...." (v.16)

The more you open yourself to God, the more insight you gain into the person you are. This brings us to our theme of "Understanding One Another".

If you cannot hope to understand yourself fully, this must surely mean:

    * that you will never fully understand your partner;
    * that your partner will never fully understand you.

Do yourselves a big favour. Knock on the head the idea that anything less than total understanding of one another equals "failure".

Of course, some need convincing that they do *not* already understand their partner through and through! After years together it is easy for a husband or wife to assume that they know all there is to know about the other. Sadly, this is far more likely to indicate that the pair in question no longer communicate below surface level. Paul Tournier, a Christian psychologist, describes such a couple in his excellent little book, *Marriage Difficulties*.

"Courtship's beautiful curiosity has been lost. The thirst for discovery and for understanding has been dried up. The husband believes that now he does understand his wife. At the first word from her lips he makes a little sign of exasperation which means, 'You're telling me the same old story!' In the face of such a reaction how can the other dare to express herself? Yet, the less she expresses herself, the less she will be understood; the less she feels understood, the more she will withdraw into herself. The thrill of discovery has been lost. If you think that you know your wife or your husband, it is because you have given up the real attempt to discover him".[1]

Continuing the quest to understand each other is vital as you seek to "Honour Marriage". While it may be impossible to fathom completely this complex, mysterious partner of yours, you can expect to go some way towards doing so. As always, the secret is to draw nearer to the

One who does fully comprehend you both, God Himself. In this chapter you will be invited to consider two new keys to understanding one another, before looking back on discoveries you have already made during the course of using this book.

Male and Female

One of the most basic keys to understanding is so obvious that many people miss it. Men and women are different! According to Genesis 1:27, how did God create *homo sapiens*?

" ....

....

.... "

Because Mankind has been made in God's image, both manhood and femininity bear the stamp of God upon them. Furthermore men and women are equal. One is not superior or inferior, and neither is of more value than the other. In 1 Peter 3:7, the apostle urges husbands to honour their believing partners as spiritual equals. How does he express this?

....

....

....

While equal, they are nevertheless different! Peter himself acknowledges this with a passing reference to one such difference. Did you notice it? What was he referring to? In our day debate rages about the nature and extent of the differences. Some insist that there is next to no difference, while others produce rigid categories of male and female characteristics.

Here is a fun exercise to help you think about some possible differences. Thanks to a friend of ours, Lynn Cheetham, you have the opportunity of a lifetime to step on to the stage. Look through the following script before acting it out together. If you are part of a group, find a volunteer couple; the rest can be an enthusiastic audience.

Vive la différence!

Scene: the hall of a house somewhere in your town. The wife is struggling to set up a step ladder on the stairs.

Husband: Here, let me set that up. It's far too heavy for you. What are you stripping the stairs for anyway? They look OK to me.

Wife: Well, I think they look tatty, and I don't like the colour scheme—they're dark and dingy and those patterns give me the creeps, especially in the dark. They look menacing, like bloated faces and long black fingers.

Husband: I feel a mother-in-law joke coming on!

Wife: Well you may laugh, but I want this house to be our home, not just a box with someone else's left-over decor.

Husband: But that's silly. We do own the place (or the Building Society does). We've got all our own furniture in it. Besides, how much time do we spend on the stairs? I know you sit on them while

92

you're on the phone, but the other couple of hours a day you're not out here. You're just not being logical at all.

Wife: You're always being logical, but your logic will never help you understand how I feel. I don't think you care about me at all. I need you to understand why it's important to me.

Husband: Well, it's obvious isn't it? You're going to outlive me, so you want the house nice for when you're on your own. Never mind dear. Why don't you leave it to me and I'll slap a coat of emulsion on and brighten them up?

Wife: You haven't understood me at all, have you? A bodge job won't solve anything. I'd like the walls that sort of peachy colour, and a sage green carpet (Allied have got a sale on this week) and the paintwork picked out in white, and I've seen some lovely William Morris curtains in greens and browns. Then I thought of some of those old-fashioned flower prints in green frames, and then down there...

Husband: Well, since you've obviously worked it all out without me, I'll leave you to it. Sounds OK to me. Well done dear.

Wife: But I don't want you to leave it to me. I want to discuss it. What do you think?

Husband: Told you. Sounds OK to me. I've got to get those reports done for tomorrow. Hedges will go mad if I'm not ready for the meeting with Amtech.

Wife: Why couldn't you have done that before? I need your help. Why does work always come before me?

Husband: It doesn't. I work to earn money to provide you with a home. I've been promoted twice in eighteen months and you say I don't care. Nonsense!

Wife: Don't stick your chin out at me in that aggressive manner.

Husband: I wasn't.

Wife: You were!

Husband: I wasn't. Men just have naturally more protruding chins!

Wife: And bigger heads and lungs so you can be conceited and arrogant and shout down the opposition! You'll never admit you're in the wrong. It's all my fault — I should have put my foot down years ago instead of being such a doormat.

Husband: You're right dear. You should always

start as you mean to go on.

Wife: What? You're impossible!

Husband: And you're beautiful when you're
           angry. Why don't we forget the
           decorating and make mad passionate
           love instead?

Wife: Just like that?

Husband: Why not?

Wife: I sometimes wonder how two such
           different beings can even live on the
           same planet.

Husband: Are you getting philosophical or are
           you coming to bed?

Wife: We can't.

Husband: Why not?

Wife: No, it's Aunt Winnie's birthday
           tomorrow and I've not posted her
           card. You know how upset she'll be if
           it doesn't arrive.

Husband: Eh?

Wife: If you go down to the post box I'll put
           the kettle on for when you get back.

Husband: (Mutters) I'd prefer you in that new

nightie...! (Louder) OK. You win. Go
on then. Where is it?

Wife: On the table. I've put the stamp on...
          Thanks darling. I do love you.

Husband: You're not so bad yourself.

Well done! Oscars all round!

Now, look back over the dialogue together and see how many male/
female differences you can identify. When Lynn was asked to write
this script for one of our earlier Marriage Courses, she was
commissioned to cram in as many differences, whether stereotype or
subtle, as she could! Make notes in the column on the right, and as you
do, talk about how you feel about male/female distinctives. Be on the
lookout particularly for any ways in which you resemble this husband
and wife.

You may wish to compare your findings with the pointers in
Appendix 1.

We do not have the space here to look in any depth at the differences
in psychological structure and social behaviour of men and women.
However, some awareness that God has built distinctives into men and
women should help you understand one another better. For example,
when each of you responds differently to identical situations it is
probably not that your partner is awkward or weak, more often he is
simply being a man, and she is simply being a woman!

Taking the subject of romance, how do you feel about the following
statements? Having worked through the list, talk about romance in
married life. With more understanding of the way you "tick", you
could find yourselves adding more "sparkle" to your marriage.

A woman enjoys her husband expressing romantic love by:

- ☐ telling her how much he loves her (without any prompting)
- ☐ kindness, gentleness and thoughtfulness
- ☐ giving her loving personal attention
- ☐ remembering special dates and anniversaries
- ☐ loving cuddles and closeness
- ☐ "dating" her as if they were still courting
- ☐ buying her flowers (etc) without expecting sex as a reward!
- ☐ other ways

....

....

A man enjoys his wife expressing romantic love by:

- ☐ looking good for him
- ☐ telling him how much she loves him
- ☐ responding to his romantic initiatives
- ☐ cooking his favourite meal
- ☐ wearing something "sexy" in private
- ☐ loving caresses
- ☐ helping keep excitement alive between them
- ☐ other ways

....

....

God, in His genius, has made you to balance and complement one another. This makes you all the more fascinating and attractive to each other as a result.

(Leaders working with a group of couples should consult Appendix 1 for an alternative suggestion in this section.)

Trouble and Strife

Believe it or not, difficulties between you can also become an important key to mutual understanding.

Every couple faces conflict in marriage at some time or other. The important question is not how major or minor is the difference between you, but "how do you deal with it?" Sadly, when mishandled, minor problems soon become gigantic. Conversely, major problems can become positive milestones in marriage when they are resolved in a godly way. They can actually deepen your understanding of one another.

a) Areas of tension

Because you are sitting calmly together you should find this a good moment to talk about any areas of disagreement between you. Look through the following list and tick anything you identify with. Do this together, and try not to fall out about it in the process!

❏ finances	❏ the children
❏ possessions	❏ use of leisure time
❏ in-laws	❏ lack of romance
❏ work	❏ making love
❏ spiritual aims	❏ busyness
❏ hospitality	❏ attitude to opposite sex
❏ habits	❏ church matters
❏ friends	❏ others...

Behind these symptoms you will usually find there are less obvious root causes. Areas of tension tend to give you a clue to the ways in which you and your partner feel vulnerable as people. When you are able to recognise what is happening this not only helps you avoid or resolve conflicts, it also increases understanding.

Once again look down the following list, this time however, husbands are to look at the women's list and wives at the men's list. Can you identify the areas in which your partner feels particularly vulnerable?

Do this without consulting. When you have finished, show each other what you have ticked.

Men	**Women**
❑ career and work pressures	❑ feeling of little value
❑ health	❑ age or appearance
❑ sexual temptation	❑ menstrual problems
❑ feeling inadequate	❑ feeling inadequate
❑ others' expectations	❑ worry about the children
❑ providing for the family	❑ anxiety about the future
❑ spiritual headship	❑ lack of quality time together
❑ expressing feelings	❑ need of friends
❑ others	❑ others...................................

How accurate were you? Have you learned anything new about your partner or even yourself? Don't be too self-critical if your estimate of your spouse was way off target. It may indicate how little your partner usually reveals to you. On the other hand, it may show that you could be paying more attention to him/her.

It is so important that you increase your understanding of your partner. If you show no willingness to listen and express no sympathetic understanding, someone else may do so with disastrous results. Adultery does not usually start with two people lusting after each other's bodies. More often it begins with a man or woman finding someone of the opposite sex who seems to understand them more than their own marriage partner.

b) How to make matters worse!
In the Bible, David faced a variety of family conflicts, some of which he handled better than others. How well do you think he did in the following situations?

* with his brothers	1 Sam 17:16-31	....
* with his father-in-law	1 Sam 26:1-11	....
* with his wife	2 Sam 6:12-23	....
* with his son	2 Sam 14:28-33	....

It's not difficult to make matters worse, is it? Many of us have become experts at it over the years! You may even recognise yourself in some of the following animal caricatures. They illustrate just a few of the ways in which many people open their mouth and put their foot in it!

The Ostrich
(head in the sand)
"Everything's fine."
"It will all blow over."
"It doesn't really matter."
"It wasn't my fault."

The Tiger
(ferocious personal attack)
"You're always causing trouble."
"You're so stupid!"
"I'll make mincemeat of you!"
"I'll show you!"

The Mouse
(the little timid one)
"Let's not fall out."
"Anything for a quiet life."
"I give in — you win."
"I know it's always my fault."

The Elephant
(never forgets)
"I'll remember this."
"You're always doing this!"
"I've had to forgive you so often."
"I'll forgive you, but I can't forget."

The Cheshire Cat
(always smiling)
"Well, praise the Lord anyway!"
"I'll be extra-nice next time."
"It's not right to disagree."
"We're so happy, aren't we?"

The Mule
(stubborn)
"That's just the way I am."
"Don't expect me to say 'sorry'."
"Think what you like!"
"I'll never understand you."

The Crocodile
(manipulative tears)

The Hedgehog
(prickly and defensive when threatened)

"You don't love me any more."   "I don't want to talk about it."
"You'll make me cry."   "I'm not speaking to you."
"You've really hurt me now."   "I'm not staying here to listen to this!"

Take another careful look over this menagerie and then write down in order of prominence those phrases which have an uncomfortable familiar sound to them. In other words, how do you tend to make matters worse?

1...

2...

3...

4...

5...

Show each other what you have written.

Do these unhelpful responses to conflict tell you anything about one another? They may give you further clues in your quest for mutual understanding.

c) Resolving your conflicts

There is no shortage of Biblical help when it comes to resolving conflict between you. But remember, the object of the exercise in working through difficulties is more than simply dismissing unpleasantness. It is to draw closer to one another.

Read the following three passages together, and then complete your own list of principles by which you can deal with conflicts in a godly way. Some of your suggestions may come directly from the Scriptures you have read, others may not. Compile the list as a couple (or a group).

* Matthew 5:23ff; 18:15f
* Ephesians 4:26,31f
* Colossians 4:6

....
....
....
....
....
....
....
....
....

In Appendix 1 you will find twelve tried and tested principles for resolving conflicts. Compare your list with that one. Keep them in mind for the future! "Honour Marriage" by putting them into practice.

Assignment
a) Do you recognise any of the following in yourself? (Tick where appropriate)

❑ moodiness   ❑ criticism
❑ apathy   ❑ stubbornness
❑ unforgivingness   ❑ unpredictability
❑ individualism   ❑ envy
❑ lack of trust   ❑ poor listener
❑ impatience   ❑ temper
❑ super-spirituality   ❑ nagging
❑ laziness   ❑ sarcasm

- ❑ selfishness
- ❑ putting off
- ❑ flippancy
- ❑ passivity
- ❑ unfavourable comparisons

Talk these things through together. Ask your partner's forgiveness for the negative attitudes you have identified.

Take this opportunity to encourage your partner for ways in which he/she has strengthened and cared for you.

Pray together, thanking the Lord for qualities in your partner that you have grown to love and appreciate. Take turns, each praying briefly.

b) Make time to reflect on anything you have discovered about one another as you have worked through this book so far.

* Have there been facts or circumstances that have been disclosed to you for the first time?
* Have you understood the meaning or importance of something in your partner's life for the first time?
* Do you have a better idea of what your partner's needs are?
* Do you have a clearer understanding of why your partner thinks, acts and feels as they do?
* What are the most intimate secrets to have been shared by your partner during the course of reading this book?

Look back through the chapters to refresh your memory. Set aside at least an hour for this.

Notes
[1] Paul Tournier, *Marriage Difficulties*, Highland Books (1984), page 14. © SCM Press Ltd; reproduced with permission.

Chapter 8   SEXUAL INTIMACY IN MARRIAGE

This chapter is definitely private and confidential! It has been written for those who are already married and should be read by you as a couple alone. As you will soon discover, this lesson is not suitable for a group.

Where are you as you begin to read this? If at all possible, arrange for an uninterrupted hour or two. Get away from the phone, muzzle the dog and pray an "anaesthetic" prayer over your children! Choose your most private and relaxing room, and snuggle up close together. You will need your Bible open at the Song of Songs.

The chapter is divided into four sections, and if you want to make the best use of it they should be looked at on four separate occasions. You will be asked to talk together at an intimate level about your sexual relationship. You may therefore need to incorporate any relevant discoveries little by little. Enjoy it in stages!

The Song of Songs

Solomon's "best Song" (or perhaps, "the best of Songs for Solomon") is, in fact a series of erotic poems. Because of this, through the centuries some people have questioned its inclusion in the Bible. Others have justified its place by spiritualising the lovers' relationship, making it a picture of God's love for Israel or Christ's love for His church.

Not everyone is embarrassed by the sexual content of the Song of Songs. Some regard it as a collection of rural love poems, others as a series of Songs to be sung during a prolonged eastern wedding feast, while others (the poet, John Milton was one), believe it presents a drama acted out between Solomon, King of Israel (presented as an ideal lover) and his Shulammite bride.

We will be following the last interpretation throughout this chapter. If you use the New International Version of the Bible, which sets out the text as a drama, it would make sense for the husband to read the "Lover's" words, and the wife to be the "Beloved". Read the "friends" words together.

Here, in your Bible, is one entire book devoted to extolling the delights of sexual love in marriage. You will find no prudery or shame in its pages as this husband and wife enjoy one another's bodies. The message of the Song couldn't be clearer. God has given you the gift of sex as a wedding present. He intends you to enjoy it.

Part One — Desire (1:1-11)

Read verses 1-11 of Chapter 1 before going any further. It is easy to recognise this woman's desire to be alone with her husband. She longs for his kisses. There are many kinds of kiss, but the Shulammite has only one in mind. Her language is that of the lover.

Yet her anticipation of sexual intimacy is heightened in other ways too. Here, and throughout the Song, you will find that the five senses are involved in the stirring of desire. In her first short Song the young bride alludes to taste, hearing, touch and smell.

Write out verses 2 and 3 below, and then identify the senses alongside each verse.

Verse   Senses
2   "...

      ....

      ....

3 ....

....

...."

In verse 4, the Shulammite's anticipation is further increased by her longing to be, and imagining that she is already, in her lover's bedroom. Yes, it *is* all right to imagine being intimate with your spouse. Here, as in so many other areas, Satan seeks to distort God's gift of healthy desire; lusting after someone else's husband or wife is a sinful and shabby counterfeit (Matt 5:28).

One of the most obvious of the five senses, sight, is missing in the opening love song, but this is rectified when the bridegroom eventually speaks. What a man sees is very important to him. The Shulammite seems to realise this because she refers to her appearance (in verses 5-7). Life in the country has given her dark features in contrast to the delicate complexions of the "daughters of Jerusalem". She has a disarmingly positive attitude towards her looks, describing herself as "lovely". Solomon agrees! He is extravagant as he sings of her beauty, and can think of no higher praise than to compare her with the most graceful of mares. (According to 1 Kings 10:23-29, he was probably quite a connoisseur of horses.)

Write out Solomon's opening Song in verses 9-11, and then caption each verse with one of the following phrases:

* He promises to buy her special gifts.
* He notices how she has dressed and expresses his pleasure.
* He lavishes words of praise upon her and uses an intimate love-term.

Verse 9 ....

....

"..
...."

Verse 10 ....

....
"..
...."

Verse 11..

....
"..
...."

Now here are some personal questions arising out of this opening section of the Song. Take your time with them and speak gently and lovingly to one another as you talk together.

* In verse 3 the very mention of her lover's name thrills the young bride and she imagines that any woman would want to be in her place. Can you recall the early thrill of your romance? Tell each other what it was about each other that first drew out your love.

* What do you find attractive about each other, and is there anything that especially enhances the way your partner looks? The Shulammite's contentment with the way she looked was, without doubt, linked to Solomon's delight in her. How good are you, husband, at building up your wife's self-esteem with genuine words of praise and appreciation?

* This bride and groom are aroused in different ways. Go back over the verses and remind yourselves of those you have seen during this first study. What stirs desire in you for your partner?

Don't rush on to the next section. Give yourselves time to benefit from the intimate things you have been sharing.

Part Two — Arousal (1:12–2:7)
The scene shifts from the Palace courts to a more intimate setting, and with this change of scene comes a quickening of pace and passion which you will catch from reading the text together.

Verse 12 seems to suggest a meal table, perhaps the Wedding Banquet, which the two lovers leave all too quickly for the privacy of the Bridal chamber. Who can blame them? If there are other guests at this table, we are not told about them, and the newly-weds are certainly not aware of them. Their thoughts are definitely not on food!

Perhaps this whole section is, after all, set in the lovers' bedroom, with the bride recalling the growing passion between them at the Banquet as they longed to be where they are now! Read through the passage together.

Once more, in verse 13, perfume plays its part in awakening passion. The oriental "sachet of myrrh" hung around a woman's neck while she slept, and the fragrance permeated her skin and room throughout the night. On this occasion Solomon himself is like the sachet of myrrh. Not only is he attractive as a man, he draws out the sweetness and loveliness in her as a woman.

The Shulammite continues talking of her lover in the most glowing terms. Now he is compared to blossoms! Her desire is to be with him, as she might lie among the aromatic henna blossoms of the vineyards Solomon himself planted at the oasis of En Gedi. Like an oasis, his love refreshes her.

In 1:15–2:2, the two lovers begin to respond to one another in short, tender exchanges. Each listens carefully to what the other has to say, and adds further words of love until heightened intimacy and arousal is evident in 2:3-6. The bride is the speaker. She is overwhelmed with desire for her husband.

Throughout this passage you will recognise the language of married lovers, ranging from the playful to the erotic. Yet at all times they speak delicately.

Look through Chapter 1 and the first six verses of Chapter 2 and write down any tender words and phrases employed by the lovers which you like especially:

....
....
....
....
....
....
....

Now compile a list of the comparisons they use in describing each other:

....
....
....
....
....
....
....

Finally, in verse 7, we have the first of three identical warnings in the Song against the careless awakening of sexual desire — at the wrong time (before marriage) or with the wrong person (someone other than your spouse). If this is the Shulammite's honeymoon, she is saying, "I'm so glad I waited!"

Here are some questions to talk over together on this occasion.

*   Are you aware of the importance of words in your lovemaking? How do they affect you? The Shulammite is full of praise for her husband's skill as a lover. How important is vocal encouragement in your intimacies?

*   Notice the references to their Bridal Chamber. Is your bedroom conducive to relaxation and romance? Take a look at it right now. Are there ways in which you can create an atmosphere suitable for lovemaking (eg general tidiness, scented candles, lighting, music, privacy)?

*   Clearly sexual intimacy is as enjoyable for this woman as the man. Are you both able to enjoy making love? Talk together with understanding and sensitivity.

Once again, don't hurry on. You have probably done enough reading and discussing for the moment.

Part Three — Intercourse (4:1–5:1)
You are just about to read one of the most beautiful descriptions of a husband and wife making love ever written. It is the man who speaks first, extolling his wife's beauty as he caresses her.

Read the passage together.

Once again, Solomon speaks as a man of the ancient east, and so the language he uses will not necessarily be what you would choose today. But while you may smile at his comparisons, learn from this skilful lover!

Notice that he is not using his wife for his own pleasure. The description is one of a man whose aim is to give pleasure before receiving it. Sometimes a woman can feel "used" even in the marriage bed.

Here the woman is stimulated primarily by words and the man by sight as they caress one another. Most men can learn from Solomon's understanding of a woman's gradual sexual arousal. His eyes, lips and hands linger on other parts of her body before moving slowly to her more intimate parts. Husband, do you need this reminder?

In giving yourself completely to each other in this way you make yourself vulnerable. This serves to deepen the bond of intimacy between you, but it also means that your partner is fragile and must be handled with care. Whether it is by words (v.7), glances (v.9) or other means, the couple in our Song constantly offer one another loving reassurance and encouragement. In verse 8 there may be a hint of insecurity in Solomon as he yearns for his Shulammite bride not to leave any part of her devotion in her home country, but to give herself completely to him. The following verses reveal that he was not disappointed.

Solomon's wife is left in no doubt about the effect she has on her husband and of his desire for her. His words now become even more passionate and erotic as their loveplay reaches its peak. Husband, read out verses 9-15 again.

The King not only delights over his bride's beauty and allure, but adds that her "perfume" is more pleasing than any spice. Is this a reference to the natural body fragrance she emits as she is aroused and which sends a thrilling message to her lover?

112

Before reading any further in this chapter, write out verse 12. What do you think the Lover is saying in these words?

"..

....

...."

....

Using this thinly disguised metaphor of a private garden, Solomon speaks of his bride's most intimate feminine parts and the sexual delights she has to offer. She is a hidden place, never before entered or enjoyed by another. As a garden she has a variety of delicious fruits to satisfy his senses.

Having been brought gradually to the heights of desire, the Shulammite whispers urgently to her lover.

Write out her words from verse 16.

"..

....

....

...."

By his strength (north wind) and tenderness (south wind) he has drawn out her passion. She is thrilled that he is so enraptured with her. His pleasure arouses her all the more, and now she wants to give him even greater pleasure still.

With the words, "Let my lover come", she invites Solomon to enter her "garden". It is no longer locked; on the contrary, it is "his garden" and her "choice fruits" are his to taste. He enters his bride still whispering sweet words of love which maintain their excitement as they come to the height of their intimacy.

Write the Lover's words in Chapter 5:1 below.

"..

....

....

...."

Postscript:
"Eat, O friends, and drink; drink your fill, O lovers" (5:1)
Who speaks these words as the lovers are united as one flesh? Can this be the voice of God Himself pronouncing His blessing on sexual intimacy in marriage? He gives husband and wife this special gift which He wants them to enjoy. Hence, "Marriage should be honoured by all, and the marriage bed kept pure" (Heb 13:4). It is reserved for one man and woman in the covenant of marriage, and is not to be shared frivolously or deviously outside of that lifelong commitment.

Here is something to talk together about now.

What excites you most in lovemaking may not do the same for your partner. In your aim to give pleasure, offer what your loved one will enjoy. Make more than one specific suggestion to help each other in this, and put them into practice!

For example, a husband may want his wife to wear some flimsy little number when they are alone, or a wife may request background music and candlelight. Both might agree that playing around in a deep warm bubble bath could get lovemaking started with a splash!

These are somewhat cautious suggestions. You can be much more intimate and bold as you talk!

Again, we recommend that you do not go on to the next section immediately.

Part Four — Creativity (5:2–7:13)

This fourth and last passage of the Song introduces a new element to the couple's enjoyment of physical love. Solomon's Shulammite wife has shown that she can respond to her husband, but now she demonstrates that she is capable of taking the initiative too!

Some Bible commentators believe that Solomon and his wife have experienced problems in their sexual relationship after their initial ecstasy. (You may find this somewhat reassuring!) This chapter therefore marks a stage of renewed freshness and creativity in their love life, after a time of difficulty. Trials can produce some good things!

Chapter 5:2-8 suggests a disturbing dream in which the young queen finds herself refusing Solomon's sexual approaches. It is too late at night, she is settled in her bed, and furthermore, she feels neglected. Perhaps her husband has been preoccupied by affairs of state recently. By the time her passion has stirred, the dream has taken on nightmare proportions. Her lover has gone leaving a token of his devotion at the door but as she searches for him in the city, she is abused like a prostitute by the watchmen. She searches in vain. Not a pleasant dream!

Now wide awake, she decides to fill her mind with loving thoughts of her husband (5:10-16). She makes a decision not to dwell on her hurts or her husband's shortcomings, but to take responsibility for her own attitudes and behaviour. Consequently, when Solomon next approaches her (6:4-12) she has a surprise in store for him!

The Shulammite arouses her husband visually in the privacy of their bedroom by dancing before him. She knows all too well how to stimulate his passion. We can only guess at what the dance of Mahanaim involved! Read Solomon's description of the dance, beginning at 6:13.

Solomon, with pupils severely dilated, takes in the sight of his wife moving sensuously before him. If verses 6-10 of Chapter 7 are anything to go by, she did not have to dance for too long!

As the King is satisfied in his wife's arms, what does she say? Write verse 10 below.

"
....

....

....

.... "

Compare this with her words in two previous occasions in the Song of Songs. Write them out too.

"
....

....

.... " (2:16)

"
....

....

.... " (6:3)

See how her love has deepened? Possession of her lover has receded as a priority to the point where she simply delights in her husband's desire for her. In Genesis 3:16 the same word for "desire" describes a wife's tenacious, obsessive impulse to possess her husband. Here, in a marriage which honours God by giving before taking, a healthy balance is restored.

As you complete this chapter we have a longer series of questions for you. You may want to discuss them over a period of weeks rather than all at once.

* How creative are you in your lovemaking? Have you become

totally sensible, predictable and boring? Think up more suggestions for adding sparkle to your loving which are silly, unusual but extremely interesting!

* Has your love life become very intense, or can you still fall about laughing with each other? Don't take your body or your sexual "performance" too seriously. Keep a sense of humour. Husband, try reciting 7:8a to your wife. That should bring a smile to your faces!

* Has trust and sexual consideration developed between you to free a shy or tentative partner to be less inhibited? Inhibitions in some persist because the other scorns their small attempts to be more innovative.

* Talk about initiating and responding. Wife, do you have too rigid or passive a view of being a responder? What might be your "dynamic equivalent" of the dance of Mahanaim? Husband, have you learned to recognise the signs of your wife taking the initiative? She may be just a little more subtle than you!

* Have you experienced any difficulties in your sexual relationship? What have they been, and have you identified the root causes?
  - What have you learned through your difficulties? Do you have a better understanding of your partner and yourself as a result?
  - Have you resigned yourself to "living with" an unresolved ...problem? Talk about it together. What avenues of help might be ...open to you? Is there a trusted counsellor or friend you can agree ...to consult?

Sexual intimacy improves as the bond deepens between a husband and wife. As you learn to give this important part of your marriage the time and attention it deserves, you will be delighted with the result. If you are newly-weds, and sex has been more difficult than you imagined, take heart — the best is yet to be!

Making love with the same fascinating person for the rest of your life is so much more exciting and satisfying than having a series of furtive affairs with comparative strangers (see Prov 5:15-20). So say to your partner, as the Shulammite did, "...at our door is every delicacy, both new and old, that I have stored up for you, my lover" (7:13).

Assignment

The words of 7:11-13 seem to be a continuation of this couple's session of lovemaking. Choosing her moment perfectly, the queen suggests a vacation away from the city. Solomon needs a break and she longs to visit her beloved countryside. What is more, she still has romance in mind! A second honeymoon!

Is there somewhere special you would love to visit or return to — just the two of you? Think about it together as your assignment. Plan a second honeymoon.

What about the practicalities (eg children, pets, finances, diary, timing)? Don't be easily discouraged. If a week (or longer) is impossible, how about a weekend or midweek break? Do you have friends or contacts who can let you have an inexpensive cottage or home? If you cannot make it soon, think positively — you have even more time to plan and anticipate how you will spend your second honeymoon!

Chapter 9   GOOD MANAGERS

If you have come to this chapter feeling harassed by time or money pressures then begin with a simple exercise. If you are not feeling like this, do the exercise anyway!

1. Relax in your chair. Beginning with your toes, tense each part of your body in turn before relaxing it. Work on up to your ears; yes, wiggle your ears and then relax them!

2. Breathe in slowly and deeply as far as you can manage comfortably. Hold your breath for a few seconds before breathing out very slowly in a controlled way. Do this several times.

3. Finally, imagine yourself walking slowly in the hills above the Sea of Galilee with Jesus. Feel the sun, smell the blossom, listen to the birds. See yourself sitting on the hillside overlooking the lake talking to Him, listening to Him. Fix your mind on Jesus. Think about His love for you.

Where possible, play some soothing instrumental music on disc or cassette. The albums of classical praise guitar music called, *The Touch* and *Such Love* could be just right. Try this exercise now. Where you are part of a group, let the leader read out the instructions.

Some of you will be reading this sentence after having dropped off to sleep!

Now, on to the business at hand. Honouring Marriage involves some down-to-earth issues. In this chapter we are looking at the very considerable challenges presented by time and money pressures. How can you be good managers of both in your marriage?

Managing Your Time Together

Time pressure is one of the most common areas of difficulty for Christian couples. If the two of you are out working during the day it may sometimes appear that you rarely have time to sit down and relax together. Make a list of the various responsibilities and tasks that you have to cope with (before and after 9 a.m.-5 p.m.).

....

....

....

....

....

....

Should God have made more hours in the day and days in the week, or are there other explanations for the time pressure you experience? Here are a few possible explanations. Can you think of others?

* We have a particularly hectic weekly schedule.
* The pace of life in the twentieth century creates pressure.
* Our lives are run by other people,
    or circumstances beyond our control.
* We are disorganised and muddle along.
* We waste time or do not make the best use of the time we have.
* As Christians we have more commitments than other couples.

*...

*...

Turn to Mark Chapters 4 and 5. It is not entirely clear when Jesus' day ended (at 4:41 or 5:20). Whichever is the case, here we have two typically action-packed days in the ministry of Jesus. Share the reading of these chapters as a couple (or a group) and then list the activities in these breathtaking days!

1..

2..

3..

4..

5..

6..

7..

8..

Although Jesus did not have exactly the same pressures that you feel today, He was constantly in demand. How then did He manage His time? He did not appear to live under the tyranny of the clock (or sundial!). On the contrary, He was master of His hours. What principles of time management did Jesus live by? Here are eight specific principles arising out of His example.

1. Give God your best time

It is always a false economy to neglect spending time with God, alone or together as a couple, because you are too busy. Jesus seems to have worked on the principle that the busier He was the more vital prayer became.

You will find a good example of Jesus giving God His best, rather than His left-over time, in Mark 1:35.

"..

....

....

...."

121

Why do you think time with God turns out to be such a wise investment when you have a busy schedule ahead? Talk about this together.

The apostle Paul was keen to see believers using their time effectively. "Live life, then, with a due sense of responsibility, not as men who do not know the meaning and purpose of life but as those who do. Make the best use of your time, despite all the difficulties of these days. Don't be vague but firmly grasp what you know to be the will of the Lord" (Eph 5:15-17; JB Phillips paraphrase).[1]

2. Identify your priorities
As husband and wife you need to be clear about what is most important to you in life. When you are united in these priorities, any pressure that could come from pulling in opposite directions is dealt with at source.

Without looking at your partner's answers, go through the following list, ticking the box when you see any "life-priority" you hold. Then go over those you have ticked and number them in importance. You will probably find this stage difficult. It is often hard to distinguish between the good and the best.

(√) (Number)
- ❑ .... making lots of money
- ❑ .... building a good marriage
- ❑ .... personal fulfilment
- ❑ .... security of the children
- ❑ .... knowing God better
- ❑ .... success
- ❑ .... a happy life
- ❑ .... commitment to local church
- ❑ .... ideal home
- ❑ .... being the best I can be
- ❑ .... surviving!

❑ .... doing God's will
❑ .... sharing the Gospel with others
❑ .... early retirement
❑ .... others...

When you have done this, share your responses with your partner.
How do they compare? Talk together about:

* any glaring differences in your top three priorities
* whether your present lifestyle and use of time are in line with your
  priorities.

Give yourself enough time to discuss this. Make it a priority!

Jesus was clear about His priorities in life. Write out the following
verses, each of which states His priorities.

"..
....
....
....
....
....
...." (Luke 4:18,19)
"..
....
...." (Luke 19:10)

These priorities affected Christ's use of His time. He would not be
distracted from them. Read Mark 1:36-39 for an early example of this
in His ministry.

3. Plan your time

Jesus did not own an expensive management diary but He had a clear timetable of goals and plans for fulfilling His priorities.

On some occasions He displayed supernatural knowledge of coming events. See how specific He was in Mark 10:32-34! On other occasions He simply planned ahead, as in Luke 9:51,52. What about the following two examples? Are they an example of good planning, or supernatural knowledge, or a combination of the two?

Luke 19:28-32   ....

Luke 22:7-13   ....

Whatever the answer, Jesus appears to have planned ahead. Do you use a diary to help you plan your time? If not, you should consider it. You do not have to become a Filofax-carrier (sounds like a disease, doesn't it!?) to make a diary work for you. The simplest, least expensive diary could become an invaluable means of helping you to plan the best use of your time:

    avoiding muddle
    looking ahead
    building in priorities
    remembering things to do
    giving an overview
    preventing others imposing their timetables on you.

4. Share time

Sometimes couples complain that they do not see enough of each other, and yet overlook simple ways of redressing this problem by sharing activities and time.

How many suggestions can you add to the following?

*   Take an interest in each other's hobbies, sports etc.

* Share jobs and chores together (name some!).
* Look for ways of serving together in the ministry of your local church.

* ....

* ....

* ....

While Jesus had time alone and knew that there were things He alone could do, He shared much of His three-year ministry with twelve disciples.

5. Rescue time
Be honest; all of us have wasted time or not made the best use of the time available to us. Some may even have been guilty of first-degree murder by "killing time"! You will look through a concordance in vain to find any such language in Jesus' vocabulary.

How and when are you likely to squander precious time? Talk about it. Are there ways in which you can rescue any of this time?

Some of your wasted time can be rescued by being put to work, while other time can be turned into recreation.

6. Relax!
Confusion can arise between wasted time and leisure time. The two are very different. One diminishes you and the other is recreative; one drains you and the other is refreshing.

In the midst of His busy schedule, Jesus found time to relax. He and His disciples walked in the countryside, sometimes for days on end. They also enjoyed sailing. Look up Mark 6:30-32 and write out Jesus' words to His disciples.

" ....

....

...."

At first sight it would appear that their plan was thwarted by the ever-demanding populace (verses 33 and 34), until you realise that their "solitary place" could have been the Sea of Galilee itself. Those of you, like ourselves, who have sat in a motionless boat at the centre of this beautiful stretch of water know just how peaceful it is. Time planned into your schedule to relax together is important. How did God Himself demonstrate this principle at the beginning of time?

"..

....

....

...." (Gen 2:2)

Jesus' opposition to legalism concerning the Sabbath should not be interpreted as opposition to the need for a day of rest. If you want to enjoy God together, work efficiently, remain healthy, deepen your relationship, make friends, see the beauty of God's world, and avoid becoming a complete bore — you need leisure time. Enjoy it to the glory of God!

7. Give your time some space!
While some people need to be more disciplined in their use of time, others go to the opposite extreme. Wanting to make the most of every minute, they pack their day so full that there is little "space" to be flexible or respond to unforeseen needs. They also give themselves a heavy weight to carry.

You may have come across this kind of person in magazines, where an individual describes a typical day in their life. One such woman, in her early thirties, married with two daughters, described her timetable:

She rises at 6.00 a.m. to shower and then organises breakfast and the girls' packed lunches, before driving them to school and waving goodbye to her workbound husband. At 9.30 a.m. she begins two hours' market-share analysis. During tea and toast at 11.30 a.m. she sorts through papers for the Open University Course she has undertaken, and then she studies or continues work on the novel she is writing until 2.00 p.m. She then paints until her alarm clock sounds at 3.00 p.m. (Her pictures have been selling following her first art exhibition.) Having collected the girls from school and given them a snack, she transports them to Brownies, ballet, piano lessons etc. After their tea, between 6.00 and 7.00 p.m., she often has clients arrive at her home for hair cutting and styling. (She once owned a successful London salon.)

At 7.15 p.m. she has her saxophone lesson! Her husband is rarely home before 8.00 p.m. They eat around 9.00 p.m., when they talk and unwind together. When he nods off on the sofa, she manages another hour or so on her studies, before waking him with a cup of hot chocolate. Having packed her husband off to bed, she may, if feeling inspired, go on sketching until midnight. She has a list of ten personal ambitions and is presently making progress with number seven, sculpture.

Having read such a timetable, you may be midway between admiration and a nervous breakdown! In what ways does Jesus' model of the use of time differ from this one?

8. Be sensible about sleep
If you constantly feel tired you will find time pressures unbearable. What did Jesus do in His busy day in Mark 4? Read verses 35-41 and write out verse 38.

"...

....

....

...."

Some nations are very sensible — they allow for a siesta! That may not be possible for you, but you too need to be sensible about the amount of sleep you allow yourself. Too much, as well as too little, can leave you tired. Do you need to make any adjustments here? For example, could you retire to bed and rise earlier?

Managing Your Money Together
Money matters are very important in marriage. We recommend therefore that you read John Houghton's book in this "How to..." series called *Handling Your Money* [2]. Because he has covered the ground so thoroughly and from a very practical perspective, this section will be brief.

Finances can be a source of real anxiety or the cause of serious disagreement to many, particularly when accommodation costs are exorbitant or unemployment rears its head.

Whether or not this has been your experience, have you been united in your attitude to money management? For instance, how do you feel about these issues?

* All our material resources and possessions belong to God.
* Regular and sacrificial giving is a priority even when finances are tight.
* A family budget — should it be weekly, monthly, annual?
* Getting into debt — is it inevitable or avoidable?
* Should we have joint or separate bank accounts?
* Should a wife work — before and after children?

1. All our material resources and possessions belong to God
Job had been a healthy and wealthy man until Satan stripped him of everything except his life to test his devotion to God. When God broke His silence to speak, shortly before restoring Job's prosperity, this is

what He said:

"...

....

...." (Job 41:11)

Covetousness, the root of man's rebellion against God (Gen 3:6), and "Mammon", the power behind money (Matt 6:24), whisper the very opposite in your ear. They present money, possessions, wealth and comfort as your rights, and ultimately as alternatives to God Himself. Anything you possess as a Christian couple is from God, to be used unselfishly. Write out 2 Corinthians 9:8.

"...

....

....

...."

2. Regular and sacrificial giving is a priority even when finances are tight

It is tempting to think that you are being responsible by cutting back on your giving to the local church when times are hard. The Bible says the opposite — it is irresponsible! Write out Proverbs 11:24,25.

"...

....

....

...."

Next, turn to 2 Corinthians 9:6. This states the same principle in the form of a helpful picture.

"...

129

....

....

...." "

When you give to God, you sow. At first sight, such giving is "lost" money, time, energy etc. But it is not; it has been sown. The smallest seed is packed with potential. By sowing generously, with faith, into the Kingdom of God, you are investing your resources wisely.

3. A family budget
There is no biblical proof text which requires you to have a budget for your finances, although prudent management of your money is taught throughout the Scriptures. Consult the following verses in Proverbs and write them below.

" ....

....

...." (Prov 13:16)

" ....

....

...." (Prov 21:5)

If you do not have a weekly, monthly or annual budget, we recommend John Houghton's chapter entitled "Good Housekeeping" in *Handling Your Money*. Consider it seriously.

4. Getting into debt
Behind debt lies the question, "Who is your master?" Just as dependence on drugs, alcohol etc. prevents you from being a free man or woman, so debt can end up enslaving you. Write out Luke 16:13,14.

" ....

....

....

....

....

....

....

....

...."

If Mammon cannot lure you by luxury it will trap you by poverty. So, what did Paul teach in Romans 13:8?

"...

....

...."

Where you have already bought goods on credit you must honour your debts and repay them on time. Whenever possible, however, avoid the lure of purchase by instalments. Your credit card may not turn out to be such a flexible friend!

Getting into debt is easier than getting out of it. If you feel as though you are already in a debtor's prison here are a number of suggestions.

1. Repent of any sinful attitude or action that has put you in serious debt.
2. Pray for God's help, especially where finding employment is the key.
3. Come to terms with the fact that, for the foreseeable future, you will have to forfeit certain comforts and extras.
4. Destroy your credit cards and do not borrow any more money.
5. Work out a careful but realistic family budget and keep to it.

Include giving in your budget!

6. Seek expert help to assess your situation and plan a strategy for repayment in stages.

7. Be open with your pastor and group leaders. When they see that you are acting with seriousness of purpose, they will make sure that you and your family do not end up cold, hungry or homeless!

8. Do all these things together. Do not hide any facts from one another. Face it as a twosome and you will deepen your relationship rather than damage it.

5. Joint or separate accounts

Remind yourselves of the heart attitude of the church in Jerusalem which included married couples!

"..

....

....

....

...." (Acts 4:32)

If you want bank or building society accounts in separate names, ask, "Why?" Is it because...

* your parents did it this way?
* you are still thinking of yourself as a single person?
* you think the man should be in charge of the finances?
* it is more practical?
* one of you is not very reliable with money, or there is a lack of trust?
* you are not sure you are together for life?
* another reason?

6. A working wife

All wives work — usually very hard indeed! This, however, concerns those who have full or part-time employment.

At the close of Proverbs an impressive woman is introduced. Read 31:10-31. If ever there was a good manager she was one! But did you notice that, as well as her outstanding qualities as a wife, mother, homemaker and "sister of mercy", she was also a shrewd businesswoman? Write out below the ways in which she was capable of generating income (See verses 16,18 and 24).

....

....

....

....

....

....

More Christian wives are money-earners today than probably ever before. Many have skills, qualifications and expertise which are vital in the community. Some find it essential to work because their husband is low-paid or unemployed. Others have chosen to work for a variety of reasons (encouraged by their husband), eg because they have not been able to bear children, or their children have gone to school or college.

But are there times when both husband and wife as earners proves to be unhelpful? Think about the following attitudes and circumstances.

* The wife feels worthless unless she is earning.
* The marriage begins to show the strain.
* The children's needs are neglected.
* Fellowship with other Christians and active involvement in the life of the church are sidelined.

* The wife's health suffers because she has taken on too much.
* The home becomes a dormitory.
* The motive is simply to increase disposable income.

The financial benefits of a second income are surely outweighed by the harmful effects of any of these factors. What do you think?

....

....

....

....

Assignment
Without reference to your spouse, look over this chapter briefly and identify one area of time management and one area of money management where you feel the need to make progress. Having written these down, compare your choices and talk about any adjustments you may need to make as a couple.

Notes
[1] JB Phillips, *The New Testament in Modern English*, Revised edition, Harper Collins (1972).
[2] John Houghton, *Handling Your Money*, Word (UK) Ltd., 1987.

Chapter 10 INCLUSIVE LOVE

Books on marriage backfire if they produce husbands and wives who are selfish and insular in their love. While there are intimate aspects of marriage which cannot be shared with anyone else, there are other ways in which couples can include others. This is the meaning of "Inclusive Love".

This chapter will encourage you to bring the strength and security of your marriage to enrich others' lives. You will not Honour Marriage if you become so wrapped up in each other that no one else seems to matter.

Your home usually reflects whether Inclusive Love has an integral place in your marriage. Take a look at the list below. Which of the following best describes the atmosphere in your home? You may choose just one, or decide on a combination of two or three. Tick the appropriate boxes without any reference to your partner at this stage.

❏ castle   ❏ oasis
❏ cafe   ❏ nursery
❏ palace   ❏ railway station
❏ guest house   ❏ museum
❏ others
....

Having done this, explain in a few words why you made your choice(s). What is it about the places above that resemble your home?

I chose...because...................

....

....

Are there any of the pictures in the list which you *wish* you could use in a description of your home? What about something not included in the list? Specify which, and explain your reason briefly.

....

....

....

....

Show each other what you have written, and talk about your choices. How do you feel about your partner's choices? Give yourselves ten to fifteen minutes for this.

How do the pictures you have chosen portray your home? Indicate below at which end of the scale you would put the following words as they apply to your home. Do this together, talking it through. What is "just right" or "moderately frenzied" for you may be very different for another couple!

	Very	Moderately	Just Right	Moderately	Very	
Quiet	....	....	....	....	....	Noisy
Showpiece	....	....	....	....	....	Messy
Closed	....	....	....	....	....	Open
Calm	....	....	....	....	....	Frenzied
Boring	....	....	....	....	....	Busy
Unwelcoming	....	....	....	....	....	Welcoming

Now consider some specific examples of Inclusive Love in marriage. The first applies to those of you with children at home.

1. As Parents

In a fascinating feature article in *The Independent*, journalist Angela Lambert examined the different attitudes to marriage of the women in one family.[1] Here are two excerpts taken from separate interviews, first with the mother and then her married daughter.

Mother

"For me, wifehood always came first, before motherhood. I wouldn't let the children monopolise me. Peter was my life. I loved being pregnant and having children, but Peter always came first and has never ceased to do so. I loved being a magistrate, loved being in local government, found it all very fulfilling."

Daughter

"Growing up with blissfully happy parents, you never think that your own marriage might be difficult. Yet as children, the four of us were very much on the outside. My mother felt a wife's job was to defer to and defend your man and she always said, 'Dad comes first'. I was sometimes dumped with my grandmother or left with highly unsuitable *'au pairs'*. We were always secondary to their relationship. It wasn't that they didn't want children — Mum loved babies and Dad liked the idea of a large family. And yet I always knew that Mum wanted to get rid of us as soon as possible."

Clearly the daughter did not feel "included" — in fact, the very opposite. Her parents' love for one another was never in doubt, but she felt on the outside — an intruder.

As a couple (or group) use this example as a case study, looking for any clues to the parents' failure to make their daughter feel included in their love. Take as much time as you need.

It would be easy to reach a false conclusion from such a case study. The answer is not to neglect or relegate your partner to give all your time to the children. You need to make your marriage the priority —

but, for your children's sake, as well as your own. Let the good things in your relationship as husband and wife overflow to your sons and daughters.

Glance at a few Biblical case studies. Each one, in its own way, is an example of inclusive parental love. The children in these verses are certainly not "on the outside".

The loving father in Jesus' parable
"'My son', the father said...

....'" (Luke 15:31)

Job remembers his happiest times
"Oh, for the days when...

....

....

...." (Job 29:4,5)

Biblical instruction in the home
"These commandments that I give you today are to be.....................

....

....

....

....

....

...." (Deut 6:6,7)

Brought to Jesus
"People were bringing...

....When Jesus

138

saw this, He...He said to them....................

'...

.... "'

(Mark 10:13,14)

"And he took ....

.... " (Mark 10:16)

Here are some very personal questions to help you begin to talk together about your own relationship with your children.

* Are your children aware of your love for one another? How do they know this? Be specific.
* Many children feel unwanted even when their parents do love them. How good are you at communicating your love to them? How do you go about it?
* Do you enjoy your children? In what ways?
* When did you last devote quality time to each of your children individually? What did you do together?
* Do you have demanding or non-demanding children (or some of each)? Are the more placid ones getting enough of your attention?
* Do you ever show favouritism in a way which makes your other children feel on the outside?
* Do you include your children's needs in:
  - your regular prayers?
  - the use of your leisure time?
  - decisions that affect their school careers?
  - number of evenings out?
  - your church commitments?
  - the decor and furnishings in your home?
* How can you show that you still love and value your teenagers while allowing them to develop apart from you?

2. As Partners

In the New Testament, Aquila and Priscilla are an excellent example of Inclusive Love in marriage. In fact they are always named together. You should not take this to mean that they were never out of each other's sight, or that they had no individual identity, but that they were a partnership. They were a very good team. The apostle Paul described them as his "fellow-workers in Christ Jesus" (Rom 16:3).

Furthermore, they were full and equal partners. Priscilla's name was not tagged on to her husband's as a courtesy gesture! On the contrary, she is often named before Aquila, leading some interpreters to conclude that she was the more able or gifted partner.

Above all, they used their home to serve God. What kind of home did they have? Look up the following passages of Scripture and identify the different ways in which their home was utilised.

Acts 18:1-3

....

....

....

Acts 18:18-21

....

....

....

Acts 18:24-26

....

....

....

....

....

....

Aquila and Priscilla were constantly on the move! First they were in Rome, then Corinth, followed by Ephesus (Acts 18). Later they appear to have returned to Rome (Rom 16:3f) and then moved to Ephesus once more (2 Tim 4:19).

It is possible that their business meant they had several bases in key cities, but it is more likely that they moved on as part of their commitment to the advance of the Gospel. There is never any mention of any children; if they were childless, this would be a factor in their ability to travel. Whatever the reason, Aquila and Priscilla's mobile home was used to serve God and welcome others wherever they lived. There was nothing cosily self-satisfied about Aquila and Priscilla's marriage. They were yoked together to serve God and others as members of a radical pioneering New Testament church.

As a couple you too can Honour Marriage by making yours a partnership dedicated to the purposes of God.

Write down in the appropriate column below the ways in which you are already serving God and others together. Then record any additional ideas for serving together you might want to consider.

Partners now in: | **New ideas:**

How does your marriage rate as a partnership? Do you need to make any adjustments as a result of the example of Aquila and Priscilla? How important in your marriage is commitment to your local church and its ministry?

3. As Friends

Friendships also have their place in Inclusive Love. But first, what about the two of you? Are you good friends? To help you think about this in a down-to-earth way, answer the questions in the following self-assessment exercise.

Which of the following words would be especially appropriate to use of your relationship as husband and wife?

☐ togetherness	☐ affection	☐ care
☐ camaraderie	☐ rapport	☐ companionship
☐ cherishing	☐ understanding	☐ compatibility
☐ trust	☐ loyalty	☐ warmth
☐ fun	☐ confiding	☐ respect
☐ helping	☐ closeness	☐ depending
☐ belonging	☐ enjoyment	☐ relaxation

If you could choose only three, which would they be?

....

A vital key to friendship is sharing.

a) How much time do you share in an "average" week — just the two of you?

daytime.........................

evenings........................

weekends.......................

Do you need to set aside more time?

142

b) Do you share family-life tasks? Indicate where appropriate.
- ❑ gardening
- ❑ household chores
- ❑ shopping
- ❑ decorating
- ❑ cooking
- ❑ others ....

c) Do you share any interests and activities?
   Write below what they are (eg sports, music, hobbies, literature, recreations)

....

....

d) Do you have an annual holiday? Yes/No
   Who takes the initiative over arrangements?...................................
   What are the main considerations in deciding what kind of holiday you have?
- ❑ money
- ❑ distance to travel
- ❑ children's needs
- ❑ my preferences
- ❑ my partner's preferences
- ❑ climate

   Other considerations...

   What about this year?...

So much for your own friendship. Clearly it is a vital factor in married life. But what about other friendships?

Some husbands and wives who describe themselves as "best friends" cut themselves off from others; they say that they do not need or want anyone else. But what begins as contentment can end as selfishness, and what starts out as privacy can finish as isolation. The fact is, the happiest of couples need other friendships; and others need the friendship of such couples.

Another look at Aquila and Priscilla will show how a secure marriage makes room for other friendships. Their friendship with Paul, a single man, proved to be deep, lifelong and enriching for all concerned.

Complete the following verses of Scripture and notice some different aspects of the friendship.

"Paul... and because......................................

....as they were, he......................................

and..."(Acts 18:2,3)

Paul stayed on in Corinth for some time. Then he left the brothers and

sailed for Syria,...Priscilla and Aquila ...They

arrived at Ephesus, where Paul ...." (Acts 18:18)

"Greet Priscilla and Aquila, my .... in Christ.

They...for me. Not only I but all the churches of the Gentiles are grateful to them" (Rom 16:3,4)

Aquila and Priscilla made friends wherever they went. This is hardly surprising when you consider their open home, loyalty, adaptability and care for others. There is not a hint of selfishness about this couple — and that gave them a capacity for making and maintaining excellent friendships.

Here are a few more questions to complete the self-assessment exercise on friendship:

Do you have good friends of your own?	YES/NO
Does your partner have good friends?	YES/NO
Do you have good friendships with other couples?	YES/NO
Do single friends come in and out of your home?	YES/NO
Do you give each other "space" in your relationship?	YES/NO
Do any of your friendships worry you?	YES/NO
Do any of your partner's friendships worry you?	YES/NO
Is your partner your best friend?	YES/NO

Show each other your responses and talk them over together.

The world needs to see and feel the impact of joyful and secure Christian marriages. Reach out in love to those around you as parents, partners and friends. As you do so you will find that a delightful principle of giving will begin to operate. Look up Luke 6:38 to see what this is!

Assignment
Look at Psalm 68:5 and Luke 14:12-14. What about your attitude towards those in need? Are you able to include those who are neglected or avoided by others? Take time to talk about this together. Are there people you know in the following categories that you can begin to pray for and reach out in love to?

- ☐ the fatherless (or motherless)
- ☐ widows (or widowers)
- ☐ the lonely
- ☐ single parents
- ☐ long-term ill (physical or emotional)
- ☐ crippled or disabled (physically or mentally)
- ☐ the unpopular
- ☐ the poor and disadvantaged
- ☐ recent immigrants

According to Jesus, these people are your neighbours (Luke 10:25-37).

Notes
[1] Angela Lambert, "For Better, For Worse", *The Independent,* Wednesday 17th October 1990. Extracts reproduced with permission.

Chapter 11   PRIORITIES, GOALS AND PLANS

This final chapter, though shorter than the rest, could be the most important one in the book. Its aim is to help you know where to go from here.

It is all very well reading a book on marriage, even one as personal as this, but if at the end of it your marriage has not benefitted in tangible ways, then the exercise can hardly be deemed a success. In fact more knowledge about marriage, or even of one another, could be counter-productive. What you have learned needs to be worked into your life together, otherwise one or both of you could end up frustrated and disillusioned. It really is up to you! Having come to this point in the book you have an ideal opportunity to improve your marriage. By giving serious attention to those things you have learned and by making specific adjustments, the weeks of using this workbook could be a wonderful investment of time.

Priorities
First of all you need to be clear about the issues which are of greatest importance and relevance to you. What priorities have you identified from the previous chapters? For example, in the chapter on communication, what discoveries did you make when comparing your self-assessment exercises? Were there levels of communication you needed to develop or was there a particular means of communication you needed to make progress with?

Right now, turn through the ten chapters together and identify any priorities that became evident as you worked through each one. Take your time because this is an important task. Talk through any "grey" areas and agree together before writing these priorities down in the centre column of the following table.

Chapter	Priorities	Order
Foundations		
Marriage Vows		
Covenant Love		
Communication		
Prayer		
Family Connections		
Understanding		
Sexual Intimacy		
Good Managers		
Inclusive Love		

Don't be too daunted by the length of your list — you have the rest of your married life to work on it! Nor should you feel awkward about having identified nothing in some chapters. Just give thanks to God and aim to extend your excellence in that area to other dimensions of your marriage.

The next step is to prioritise your priorities! What does that mean? Having made your list, you need to give each item on it a "batting" order. Which of these priorities are most important, perhaps even vital? Do you need to make progress in one area before you can tackle another? Is there a degree of urgency about any of these priorities which may determine its place in the order?

Go through the list in your table together and write a number in the right-hand column to indicate the order of importance alongside each priority. Number One will be the first item for action on your agenda! You may be able to work at more than one item simultaneously.

Goals
Now you are ready to set yourself specific targets to aim for in each area of priority.

A trap many fall into at this point is to aim for unrealistic or superficial goals. For example, a couple who need to give more attention to talking together might set themselves a goal of talking to one another for an hour every day. They manage it for a few days before a particularly hectic schedule or an unexpected caller interrupts. They miss their hour and feel failures. After a few more days they begin to be more aware of the clock than they are of talking together, and finally as conversation falters they abandon the whole business because it is too much for them.

Their goal was unrealistic even if their priority remains a vital one. Far better to aim at a humble ten minutes a day and weave that into the pattern of their life together than go for an impressive hour and end up with nothing at all.

But there is a more important question to ask. Was their goal really a goal, or was it more like an action plan? This couple need to think more deeply about their priority of talking together. Were they really just aiming to talk for an hour irrespective of the quality of their conversation? What was the purpose of talking more? The answers to these questions will be reflected in the goals they set.

Here is one possible suggestion for our imaginary couple. You will see that it incorporates a well-proven key to effective goal-setting (ie deciding on long- medium- and short-term goals). The long-term goal is, of course, what they are working towards to fulfil the priority they have identified.

	Priority No.1 We need to talk to each other more
Short-term goal	To tell each other about our day so that we are "in touch" with each other's lives.
Medium-term goal	To talk about family issues lovingly and responsibly.
Long-term goal	To open up our deepest feelings to one another.

These goals indicate that thought has been given to the meaning and purpose of talking to each other, and that the couple are approaching their ultimate target in stages. These stages may vary in duration. Sometimes they will merge into one another so that you are hardly aware that the long-term goal is within your grasp.

Now it is your turn. Using the same Priority Box work slowly through your list of priorities and set yourselves goals. Decide on your long-term goal before setting medium- and short-term goals. Make rough copies of the Priority Box and when you are satisfied with your targets, write them in your diary or a special notebook.

Priority No.

Short-term goal	
Medium-term goal	
Long-term goal	

This goal-setting stage should take you quite a long time. Don't rush it. Take it at your own pace, perhaps over a series of evenings or a weekend. Only proceed to the planning stage when you are clear about your goals.

You will find this process of establishing goals to be an ideal focus for your praying together. Seek God's will for every dimension of your marriage, and then you will be able to go for your goals with the confidence that comes from faith.

Plans
Welcome back! Having completed your goal-setting you are now ready to form an action plan. The aim is to plan a campaign which will take you to your desired goals.

Here are four questions to ask as you form your plans.

a) Are they specific? Vague and imprecise plans will go no further than your writing paper! Plans should have specific answers to questions such as "when?" and "what?"

b) Are they practical? Be down-to-earth. Make plans that answer the question "how?" What resources or adjustments will be necessary to carry out your plans?

c) Are they simple? Don't be over-complicated! The simpler the better.

d) Are they realistic? Just as your goals needed to be achievable, so too do your plans. Don't make impossible demands of yourselves, and be realistic about the difficulties you could face.

Beginning with Priority Number One make a plan for each of your short-term goals. You are not ready to make plans for the medium and long-term goals at this stage. Before you start take a look at the plan in the diagram. It continues the example used throughout this chapter.

Priority 1   We need to talk to each other more

Goals

Short-term	Medium-term	Long-term
To tell each other about our day so that we are "in touch" with each other's lives. Make the evening meal a time for chatting about the day — no more trays in front of the TV! When this is impossible — Horlicks and ten minutes before bedtime.	To talk about family issues lovingly and responsibly.	To open up our deepest feelings to one another.

Plans

If you find our diagram helpful then use it. You may prefer to design one that suits you better.

With these and future plans employ the following strategy to ensure success!

1. Start your plan as soon as possible. Why not today or tomorrow?
2. Give yourself to it with total enthusiasm.
3. Refer to your goals regularly. You need to remind yourself of the purpose behind your actions.

4. When you find things tough or you fail, get back on course quickly. Persevere!
5. Allow God to help you and to break into your action plan.
6. Decide on dates to monitor your progress. Keep each other on course.
7. Don't move on to your next goal too soon. New habits and patterns should be well integrated into your life together, otherwise you could end up abandoning your first goal instead of building on it.
8. Form your action plan for the next stage in the light of any benefits accumulated in the earlier stage(s).

Your marriage is worth the time and concentration this chapter demands and your partner is worth the effort involved. Don't let your life together drift aimlessly. As you give serious attention to these priorities, goals and plans you will not only enrich your own relationship, you will become a much-needed example to others of *Honouring Marriage*.

APPENDIX 1
POINTERS FOR GROUP WORK AND EXERCISES

a) Possible wrong foundations in the relationship are:-

* wanting to project an image of the perfect couple
* romance, charm and fun; superficial attraction
* lack of honesty
* selfishness
* lack of trust
* no absolute commitment
* no place for God in their relationship.

b) We suggest that the following statements in the two lists indicate that the person's life is established on the foundation of Jesus Christ.
c d f i j l p r t v

c) Wanting to "sort out" your partner, or ease your guilt feelings are not the healthiest reasons for wanting to pray together as a couple!

d) We believe that each of these seven statements is a true application of what it means to "leave your father and mother".

e) Male/Female differences and caricatures in "Vive la Différence" include:

* physical strength
* female intuition and sensitivity to atmosphere
* readiness to communicate
* the importance of the home
* male tendency to be analytical
* length of life

* attention to detail
* importance of career
* physiological differences
* male aggression
* sexual arousal (instant versus gradual)
* expressing feelings

f) Leaders working with a group may want to use James Dobson's video *What Wives Wish Their Husbands Knew About Women* in the *Focus on the Family* series (Word Lifeware Video, Word (UK) Ltd, 9 Holdom Avenue, Bletchley, Milton Keynes MK1 1QR). Although a live lecture format is used, Dobson's anecdotal style sustains interest. If the full running time of 83 minutes is too long, show an extract for 20-25 minutes. A study guide to accompany the video series is also available from Word (UK) Books.

g) Twelve principles for resolving conflicts:

1. Take the first opportunity to face up to the problem, rather than put it off.
2. Deal with strong emotions first.
3. Clarify what the problem is. Establish the facts. Clear up any misunderstandings.
4. Speak to one another with love and respect.
5. Listen carefully to what your partner says, seeking to understand.
6. Accept, from the outset, that you could be in the wrong.
7. Consider whether forgiveness needs to be sought or offered.
8. Realise that, when a solution is not possible immediately, a timetable for dealing with the problem in stages may be helpful.
9. Keep Biblical principles and spiritual values in focus.
10. Make the issue a subject of prayer.
11. Be prepared to ask for help from those you both trust.
12. Convey your absolute commitment to the marriage whatever the conflict may be.

APPENDIX 2
REAFFIRMING YOUR MARRIAGE COVENANT

A wedding anniversary is a particularly meaningful occasion to reaffirm your covenant commitment to one another.

Prepare carefully for the occasion you choose. You may want to make a special meal for the two of you. If your children are of suitable age, it may be good to include them in the occasion. Husbands, don't forget to buy some flowers for the table!

Take your time with the words, and also in between one another's statements. Look at one another and speak naturally. Hold hands. The blank brackets in the text indicate where your partner's name can be used.

Pray
Thank the Lord for His presence, His love and His grace. Acknowledge Him as the Lord of your marriage and family. Ask Him to deepen your love for one another as you reaffirm your marriage vows.

Husband, say to your wife:
(   ), on our wedding day I declared before God, our family and friends that I would take you to be my wife in Christian marriage. Today, privately, I reaffirm that public pledge — to love you, comfort you, honour and protect you. I also vow to be faithful to you as long as I live.

Wife, say to your husband:
(   ), on our wedding day I too declared before God, our family and friends that I would take you to be my husband in Christian marriage.

Today, privately, I reaffirm that public pledge to love you, comfort you, honour and protect you. I also vow to be faithful to you as long as I live.

Husband:
The promises I made to you in our Marriage Ceremony were serious and unconditional. I covenanted to love you, come what may; and now I repeat that pledge to do so
— for better for worse
— for richer for poorer
— in sickness and in health.
I will love you and cherish you until death parts us.

Wife:
The promises I made to you were also serious and unconditional. I covenanted to love you, come what may; and now I repeat that pledge to do so
— for better for worse
— for richer for poorer
— in sickness and in health.
I will love, cherish and submit to you until death parts us.

Read these Scriptures to one another.

Husband   Ephesians 5:21-33

Wife   1 Corinthians 13

You may also wish to use the fourteen statements on pages 47-50 (Chapter 3) as an expression of your commitment to Christ-like love in your marriage.

Pray Together
Thank God for the past and commit your future life as a family to Him.